The Santa Fe Trail

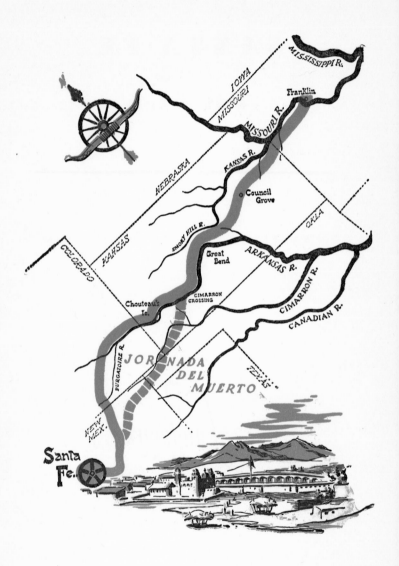

THE
SANTA FE
TRAIL

★

by **SAMUEL HOPKINS ADAMS**

Illustrated by **LEE J. AMES**

Landmark BOOKS

RANDOM HOUSE • NEW YORK

Contents

The Santa Fe Trail

1

Lost Cities

IT ALL BEGAN WITH A FAIRY TALE. ACCORDING
to this legend, an ancient Bishop of Lisbon, pur-
sued by Arabs, took ship for some unknown goal,
landed on the Pacific coast of North America,
and led his men across the mountains of the
Southwest. This, says the story, happened all of

3

twelve hundred years ago. By what route the bishop is supposed to have traveled does not appear.

Somehow they all found themselves in a pleasant and fertile country inhabited by savage Indians. The fighting bishop conquered the tribes and founded a nation called Cibola, with seven great cities. A mighty civilization developed. Each city became a treasure house of gold, silver, and jewels.

Nobody knew exactly where the cities were supposed to be, for of course there were no such cities. There was really no eighth-century churchman who crossed the mountains any more than there was a Jack who climbed the beanstalk.

But the early Spanish conquerors who took over Mexico and called it New Spain at the beginning of the seventeenth century believed pretty much everything that was told them. They probably heard stories about the Seven Cities from the Indians whom they captured. The Indians were pretty good at making up tales, themselves.

The Spaniards, passing these reports along, undoubtedly added some fancy episodes from their own imaginations. They organized treasure hunts which covered many square miles of unexplored country. They did not find Cibola, of course. But while they looked for it they had a pleasant time killing Indians wholesale. The idea seems to have been to teach the red men the superiority of the white race.

After the Spaniards had failed, the hardy frontiersmen of this country took up the search. Treasure-tales have always stirred the blood of pioneers. Even if the rumors were false, even if there were no golden cities, the stories were a good excuse for adventure.

Because of these restless and daring men, Spaniards first and Americans later, the Santa Fe Trail stretched slowly and uncertainly across the map. It opened up and developed the great, rich Southwest. But for its perils and excitements, the boundary of our country might have stopped not far west of the Mississippi River. We might not now have Texas and New Mexico and all that Southwest territory to the Pacific.

Today there are prospectors and mountaineers who still talk of Cibola. They half believe that the Seven Lost Cities may yet be discovered in some unexplored desert or mountain-blockaded land of forest and canyon.

Spain, in the 1500's, was a powerful nation. Its men were soldiers, explorers, and adventurers. One of the boldest was Cabeza de Vaca, which means Head of a Cow. Landing in Florida early in the century, he led his little band of men west to the Gulf of Mexico. Across the Gulf, he knew, lay the Spanish province of New Spain. He and his followers knocked together a boat of driftwood, stripped themselves of their shirts for sails, and made the passage more by good luck than by good sense. They were captured by Indians. From the tribal legends that he heard, de Vaca built up a picture of wonderful cities to the north.

De Vaca gathered all the information that he could. Most of it was false, but he did not find that out until later. With a few companions, he escaped from captivity. There were no maps, no trails, no compass, no guidance of any sort. Asked afterward how he set his course, he is reported to have replied that he asked the blessing of God, pointed his nose at the North Star, and followed it.

Exactly what he did find will never be known. He turned up in Mexico City with tales that made the Spaniards' eyes bug out. We can imagine the scene in the viceroy's palace when the gaunt and tattered explorer arrived with his report. The Spanish officials would be gathered in the council room to ask him dozens of eager questions.

Had he really found the lost Cibola?

Certainly. He had entered one of the cities.

What was it like?

Wonderful. The houses had roofs of gold and jeweled doorposts.

Were the inhabitants civilized?

Oh, yes! They spoke Spanish. They were skilled artisans and builders. The women were beautiful. They wore rich garments, set with precious metals and gems.

How far was this wonderful country?

Very far. Eighty, ninety, one hundred days.

Was the voyage arduous?

Terrible.

Indians?

Worse. Giants! They lived in caves in the mountains and ate the smaller Indians alive.

Was there any game?

Much. That was one of the perils. The bears were as big as elephants. There were birds of prey that could carry off a mule. (The explorer had doubtless seen some of the twelve-foot-wing-spread mountain condors of which a few still survive in the California wilds.) And in one river, three leagues wide, he had seen cow-sized fish that spouted boiling water.

There were other risks of the trail. One day the sun might be so hot that men's whiskers shriveled on their faces. The next night a blizzard would sweep down fit to freeze the blood in one's veins. Poisonous vapors jetted up from the earth. At times they had been almost smothered by clouds of steam. Oh, yes! it was a bad, bad journey. He would advise taking it only with a large military force.

From all that has come down to us, Senor Head-of-a-Cow must have been a gentleman of lively imagination.

The Spaniards swallowed it whole. One of the most excited listeners was a Francisan friar named Marcos de Niza, a man of action as well as imagination. He applied to the Spanish viceroy for permission to organize his own *atajo* (expedition) and locate the rest of the Seven Cities. He further announced his intention of converting the Indians.

Permission was given, and de Niza set out at the head of a well-armed band. He could hardly have followed the earlier explorer's route, for he came out at what was probably Pueblo, in the Rocky Mountains. For some unexplained reason he made no attempt to enter it. But he did bring back a glowing report of a great city as splendid as Madrid, and roofed in gold. Maybe he had been deceived by a mirage. Or maybe all those early Spaniards were natural-born tellers of tall tales.

Again the viceroy took it all for the truth. He sent out a large military expedition, this time twelve hundred men. The orders were to capture and annex the city for the glory of the Church and the enrichment of Spain.

The great Spanish grandee and soldier, Fran-

cisco Vasquez Coronado, then Governor of New Spain, was appointed head of the enterprise. He had already led a less ambitious journey north into the wilds. If anybody could find and take the lost cities, Coronado was the man. He polished up his gold-inlaid armor and set forth with all the style of an army.

Out in the wilds of a high desert, a lone figure mysteriously appeared. The official report calls him El Turco. He was certainly not a Turk. He may have been a half-breed or possibly a Negro. He spoke Spanish.

"What," he asked, "does the great Capitan-General seek?"

"Cibola and its lost cities," Coronado answered.

"I know all about it," the stranger said. "Its chief city is Quivira. It is lofty as the tallest pine and glistens with gold and silver."

"Where is it?"

"Many days' journey to the north," El Turco replied. "I will lead you."

After a month's travel, the expedition came out of a low pass in the foothills, in sight of a settlement of the slope.

"Is this it?" Coronado asked his guide.

"This is it," El Turco answered.

The Captain-General's eyes took in the mean little huddle of adobe huts.

"This is the wonderful city of gold and jewels?" he asked.

El Turco became uneasy. "This is Quivira," he faltered.

Coronado turned to a lieutenant. "Take this man out and hang him," he ordered.

As there was no tree handy, the unfortunate guide was strangled.

Coronado and his dwindling band strolled about for three years without finding any city worth capturing. They did find plenty of Indians whom, as was the custom of the times, they killed on sight. Near what is now Albuquerque more than two hundred savages were thus slaughtered.

Though uncivilized by Spanish standards, the red man had his own logical idea of what was right and just. From his experience of the Spanish conquistador, he came to believe that the white man was "bad medicine" to be killed if possible; if not, to be avoided. If it was right for white men to kill Indians, it must be equally right for Indians to kill white men. Doubtless the many cruelties committed by the red-skinned tribes in the following centuries were the natural result of these early Spaniards' crimes against the Indians. The savages were no worse than the apostles of civilization.

Little is definitely known of Coronado's trails, but he certainly discovered the Grand Canyon. He seems also to have ranged as far east as Kansas before making up his mind that there was little glory and less profit in that adventure. In the course of his travels, he abandoned a flock of sheep and some horses, which lived and grew up with the country. So, but for the dead Indians, he left the region better off than he found it.

Upon his return to Mexico City, Coronado asked at once for Marcos de Niza. The friar had gone elsewhere, which was doubtless just as well for him. There were plenty of trees in Mexico City, and it is not likely that his belonging to the clergy would have saved him from a noose by order of the Captain-General.

The next seeker for the Seven Cities was Don Castano de Sosa, who headed north in 1591 with an ox-cart train. The carts traveled not on wheels such as we know them, but on solid cottonwood logs. These must have been rather bumpy for the drivers. De Sosa seems to have been interested in three main lines of Indian trade—furs, salt, and turquoises. For these he was prepared to barter plumes from macaws, parrots, and other gay-hued birds. He left no record of dead Indians.

His successor did better in that respect. Don

Juan de Onate was a rich silver-mine owner. Like most rich people, he wanted to be richer. The way to do this, he thought, was to discover the Lost Cities and loot them. He financed his own *atajo*, and in 1598 set out for the unknown with eighty-three wagons rolling on round log wheels. One hundred and thirty followers bounced and jounced in the wagons.

Don Juan seems to have been an exceptionally cleanly gentleman at a time when only royalty bathed as often as once a week (and not all royalty by any means), for he took along a silver bathtub. One can imagine the astonishment of the patient oxen at the mighty jingle-jangle back of them when the wagon hit a rock.

Like his predecessors, Onate missed the fabulous cities. His fighting men, however, had an enjoyable battle with an Indian tribe, killing more than six hundred of them. As the Spaniards numbered only seventy, this was considered an unusually good performance. On his northbound trek he bypassed the pueblo which was later to become Santa Fe, but reached it on his return. In all, the expedition was gone about three years.

What the party did in the way of trade is not recorded.

Other explorers went in other directions. They found little reward, but each seems to have killed a satisfactory number of Indians. One such band founded Santa Fe in 1609. Others penetrated into the Rockies and probably got as far east as the Missouri. They left no trails, established no settlements. The only landmarks of their fruitless wanderings were the bones of their victims.

2

The Trade Hunters

AMERICANS OF A LATER DATE WERE NOT AS EAS-
ily fooled as the early Spaniards. Nevertheless, the
Cibola tales found many listeners and some be-
lievers on the frontier. It might not have been
so easy to organize expeditions into the wild, unknown regions without the dazzling prospect of

gold and silver, emeralds and rubies. The wise leaders may not have taken much stock in this sort of thing. But it was a spur to the ambition of the young and restless.

Pioneers began to get excited about the Southwest at the very beginning of the nineteenth century. As early as 1800 they followed the rivers, trapping beaver, otter, and mink; killing bear and buffalo and sometimes being killed by them. Some of them traded with the Indians: cheap trinkets and gay cloth for gold nuggets. Where did the gold come from? The Indians would not tell.

They did tell of the faraway city of Santa Fe. It was, by their accounts, a wonderful place, rich and eager for trade. Their reports fitted in neatly with the legend of lost Cibola. The trappers brought the news back to the frontier, and so to the great fur-trading center, St. Louis. It came to the ears of a prosperous trader named Morrison. Being nearly forty, he considered himself too old for adventure. But he very much wanted to set up trade with that wealthy, mysterious city.

Morrison found a strong and daring young man

of French background who was willing to act as his agent. The young man was a Creole named Le Land.

"Give me the goods and the mules," Le Land said, "and I'll get them to Santa Fe."

"There's no trail there," the trappers warned him.

"I'll make my own trail," the Creole said.

Little is known of his reckless venture except that he started out in 1804 and did get through with several mule-loads of calicoes, muslins, and woolen goods. Le Land was more enterprising than honest. He sold the trustful Morrison's goods, pocketed the proceeds, married a Spanish-Mexicana, and settled down. Mr. Morrison might whistle for his money. Le Land never came back.

So far as is known, he was the first American to make the dangerous journey from the East. He left no trail.

A year later, a James Purcell, or Pursley, turned up in Santa Fe. He was footsore; his clothing was rags and tatters. However, his "possible sack," the large bag in which frontiersmen carried such spare parts as leather patches, needle and thread, and odds and ends, was heavy with gold nuggets. The alcalde, or mayor, summoned him directly for questioning.

"Where did you find this gold?" the alcalde asked.

"Up in the Platte River country," Pursley replied. As the Platte River was a thousand miles long, this told the official all that the prospector wanted him to know, which was not much.

"Draw me a map," the Mexican directed.

"What for?" Pursley asked.

"I'll send a detachment of cavalry back with you."

"Oh, no!" Pursley replied. "That land belongs to the U. S. A." (He was probably wrong, but he meant well by his country.) "If your soldiers go up there, they'll take it over for Spain. No, sir, your Excellency!"

No amount of persuasion could move him. He did not go back to the source of the gold and died without giving up his secret. Fifty years later, when that part of the Rockies did belong to the United States, prospectors who knew about Pursley located and worked his mine.

Like those who had gone before him, Pursley left no trail.

The next known visitor from the East was the famous Zebulon M. Pike. Captain Pike, with a small squad of surveyors in uniform (they were actually soldiers) crossed the line from the Louisiana Territory into Mexico in 1806. The territory had recently been annexed, and the boundary was uncertain. The young officer may have thought that he was in his own country when he built a fort on the Rio del Norte.

The Spaniards thought differently. They rounded up the invaders and led them to Santa Fe to explain to the authorities, who wished to know what the Americano was doing on Spanish soil.

"We were just making some maps and surveys," Captain Pike answered.

"Maps to where?" the Spaniards asked suspiciously.

The Captain explained that he was interested in trade between the two nations. If he could lay out a short trail, it would help.

All very well, the Spaniards said; but wasn't he

really there to capture and annex territory to the United States?

"Why, a goat couldn't live on that land, let alone a good American," the explorer said. "We don't want it."

"Then why have you built a fort?" the questioning official demanded.

Captain Pike had an answer for that one, too. "In case of attack by the Indians," he said.

The Spaniards were not satisfied. They held him prisoner for a time, then took him on a tour to Chihuahua and other cities. Perhaps they intended to impress him with the might of New Spain. He was more impressed with the undeveloped riches of the country and the opportunities for trade.

When Pike was set free, he returned to his own country with glowing reports of business opportunities. He also explored part of the Rocky Mountains and left his name on one of them. To this day, flivvers bearing the old-time legend "Pike's Peak or Bust" whiz along at sixty miles an hour over the same route which he and his mules painfully traveled at ten miles a day.

Captain Pike may well have been telling the truth when he said that his only interest was trail-finding and trail-making. But he left no trails.

By this time the Spanish authorities were becoming suspicious of the enterprising *gringos*. They had treated Captain Pike kindly, but the next visitors got a rough welcome. A dozen traders who set out for Santa Fe in 1812 were seized and thrown into jail as spies. Of this lot who were held in captivity for nine years, there are definite records of only three. James Baird, Samuel Chambers, and Robert McKnight were set free and left to find their way back to the Missouri River as best they might. On the way, McKnight was caught and scalped by the Comanches. The other two got back to safety after severe hardships.

Thus far, the Spaniards were probably within their rights. The Americans *were* trespassers.

In the case of Auguste P. Chouteau, the Spaniards were in the wrong. Chouteau was a man of wealth and a founder of the great Missouri Fur Company. In 1810 he led a party of trappers across the Rockies. It was the first such group to spend a winter west of the mighty range.

Returning home with a rich haul of beaver, mink and otter, Chouteau organized a powerful caravan of nearly fifty men. With them he planned to work the almost untouched fur country at the headwaters of the rivers Arkansas and Platte. On the way they were attacked by a small army of the warlike Pawnees, who might have killed them. Fortunately the trappers were able to find a place of safety on a thickly wooded island in the Arkansas River. Sheltered behind the cottonwood trees, the little force poured a withering fire into the Indians. It was the savages' first experience of powder and ball. They were beaten off after heavy losses.

On the island Chouteau put up a log fort in which he left half of his force. The other half he led westward to the mountains. They were peaceably gathering pelts in the spring of 1817 when a squad of more than two hundred Spaniards surrounded the camp. Odds of ten to one were too heavy for even the hardy pioneers. There was no question of putting up a fight. The Spanish commanding officer read his orders. He was to take them to Santa Fe.

Chouteau protested. The territory in which they were operating was not Spanish. If it belonged to any nation, it was the United States. He was wasting his breath. The little band was taken to Santa Fe and thrown into jail. Some were put in irons. At one time the governor threatened to shoot them as spies. Their quarters were wretched, their food coarse and scanty. All their property was taken from them.

After holding the men prisoners for forty-eight days, the governor thought better of it and let them go. But he did not return the thirty thousand dollars in merchandise and money which he had seized.

Chouteau never liked Spaniards from that day. One can hardly blame him!

It was this sort of injustice that stirred up hard feelings among the Americans. A quarter of a century later it boiled over in the Mexican War, which brought the whole Southwest under the American flag.

Notwithstanding Spanish hostility, trade-hungry Americans continued to travel deep into Spanish territory. The Glenn-Fowler band seem to have got on well enough with the Spanish officials. They even received permission to hunt and trap. They, too, brought back "many strange and marvelous stories of inexhaustible wealth in the precious metals" to be found in the wilds.

All these ventures traveled by different routes. They left little trace for those who followed. Unless hoofprints in the sand, ashes of campfires, and bones of slain animals and enemies are to be taken for landmarks, these early pioneers were not trail-makers.

William Becknell, who came next, was. Because of his daring and enterprise, what began as a trail became a highroad of empire.

3

Captain Bill

HUNTERS AND TRAPPERS ON THE UNMAPPED
prairies sometimes ran across salt licks. Deer, antelope and buffalo haunted these places. A few
were hastily and crudely mined, and the salt from
them was brought back to the frontier towns for
sale. It is probable that salt is what first took Cap-

tain William Becknell into the wilderness. His business was that of salt-maker until he found Indian trading more profitable and interesting.

By the time the War of 1812 was settled, Becknell was a known and respected figure along the Missouri River. It is possible that he got his title of Captain at the time, though that part of the nation knew little and cared less about the fighting going on in the East and South.

Becknell had little education. In the few documents which he left, his spelling is something to marvel at. In his letters, "knife" is Knif (with a capital K), "sugar" is "shuger," and "eaeght" you can puzzle out for yourself. (Or, if you can't, it was the Becknell spelling of the verb "to eat.") But if he could not spell, he had other talents.

He could find his way through trackless country. He knew the habits of animals, Indians, and frontiersmen. These latter were rough-and-ready individualists, jealous of their independence. Nobody could tell *them* what to do or what not to do. Becknell knew how to handle them. He had the knack of quiet authority. He was shrewd, brave, hardy, and honest. Men respected him.

Even with the Indians he was honest, which was by no means true of many early traders. He did not get them drunk on the terrible, raw "trade" whiskey and cheat them. Because they passed the word along that he was trustworthy, he was able to go safely where others would have been in danger. With each venture he penetrated farther and farther west.

In the fall of 1821 he set out with a small pack train to trade with the Indians. There were only four men in the band. Their pack mules carried perhaps five hundred dollars' worth of cheap goods.

At a crossing of the Arkansas River, Becknell and his party met two mounted Mexican adventurers. The Mexicans were about to return south with a little gold and a few turquoises and semiprecious stones. These they had received from the Indians in exchange for bright-colored feathers.

What were the Americanos doing there? they asked.

Looking for Indians to trade with, Becknell said.

"Why waste trade on savages?" one of the Mexicans wanted to know.

"What else should we do with our goods?" Becknell asked.

"Bring them to Santa Fe. They will go like hot tortillas."

The Mexicans spoke of the fancy prices which the cheapest cotton cloth brought in the city. The Americanos had but to show their goods in Santa Fe's market place; they would sell on sight. But Captain Becknell shook his head. He had heard about the fate of the McKnight-Baird-Chambers expedition.

"Not me!" he stated. "I don't want to rot in a Spanish jail."

The two Mexican horsemen exchanged glances and burst into excited protest.

Hadn't El Capitan (as they called Becknell) heard? Mexico had risen against the Spaniards and driven them out. Mexico was free. Its citizens wanted nothing better than to trade with their Americano neighbors. El Capitan and his followers need fear no trouble. They would be welcomed. *Viva* Mexico! *Viva* los Estados Unidos!

It sounded good to the Becknell group. They held a council and decided to go to Santa Fe. The horsemen gave them plain directions for the trail, bade them farewell, and set out upon some private venture of their own. (Probably to take another look for the Seven Lost Cities of Cibola.)

The Americans did not find the trip a hard one. They reached Santa Fe with their merchandise in good condition. But at first sight of the place, they were sorry they had come. Everything they heard had led them to expect a lordly city of tall and stately buildings with wide streets and squares peopled by richly dressed Spaniards.

Instead they stared with disappointed eyes at a dreary stretch of low mud houses and straggling cornfields. Even the famous plaza seemed to them a poor affair with its raggedly built cathedral and governor's palace.

The people were worse than the place. Gambling seemed to be their main activity. Everybody gambled; soldiers, merchants, priests, peons, and beggars. They cast dice or dealt cards in the open streets, beneath the scraggly trees of the plaza, on the cathedral steps.

A squad of soldiers was lazily drilling before the palace. Some had no coats; others had no trousers. A few men carried long-barreled rifles, but mostly they were armed with lances or bows and arrows. Presently they wearied of the drill. Without any order from the shabby lieutenant in command, they broke ranks and sat down. Some went to sleep; others fell to playing cards.

The disgusted Americans felt certain that there would be no trade worth their while in Santa Fe. They were never more mistaken in their lives. No sooner had they led the pack-mules forward than they were surrounded by a surging, chattering, gesticulating crowd. Members of the governor's household appeared and pushed through the mob. Merchants fought for places. Eager hands helped to unstrap the packs. The soldiers got up and tried to restore some order.

What did the Americanos have to sell? Silks? Ribbons? Calicoes? Velvets? Whiskey? Nails? Rope? Pepper? There was a pressing demand for all of them. Also for tea, salt, tobacco, knives, candle-wicking, starch, and brooms. It was clear to the strangers that they could sell pretty much everything in their packs. They were only sorry that they had not brought ten times as much. So were the Mexicans.

The demand was there, all right, but what about payment? These people did not look as if they had any money. Again, the newcomers were one hundred per cent wrong. There was plenty of money; gold and silver. Or maybe the *gringos* would prefer turquoises. Or emeralds, by which the Mexicans meant olivines and other semi-precious stones. The difficulty for the traders was not lack of money but a surplus of it. For every item of goods in their packs, there were twenty pushing, yelling, demanding, cursing customers.

Captain Becknell had figured that the total load of goods might be worth five hundred dollars. At the close of trade, each member of the band had that much and more. This beat salt-making, trapping, and Indian trading all hollow!

The Captain spent a pleasant winter in Santa Fe. He left with urgent invitations to come back, bringing more and better trade with him.

On the trip home he had plenty of time for thinking. His thoughts ran along simple mathematical lines. If a small pack train could make as much money as he and his companions were taking back to Missouri, a big *atajo* could make a lot more. And if mules which carried a pack of three hundred pounds, topweight, apiece, could be hitched to a wagon carrying three thousand and up, what would that figure out to? A nice, big, fat profit, Captain Becknell thought.

Wagons were the answer. But no wheel had ever turned beyond the Missouri River, headed for the Far West. Could a caravan make it? Becknell did not know. But he intended to find out. That is the kind of man he was.

4

The Outpost

AT THE EDGE OF THE TOWN OF FRANKLIN, MIS-
souri, a cloud of dust overhung a rough, tempo-
rary camp. It was a scene of activity and confu-
sion. Horses whinnied. Mules hee-hawed. Dogs
barked. Men ran here and there, shouting orders,
exchanging information, sorting out merchandise

from the piles scattered about in the dust. Above a tent the flag of the United States of America floated in the warm May breeze. The flag had only twenty-four stars, for this was the year 1822.

Inside the tent a middle-aged, stocky, restless-eyed man with a red beard and red hair sat at a raw deal table, studying an inked-in map. This was Captain William Becknell, organizer of the expedition. Hurrying men rushed in and out, asking questions and receiving directions. The next morning camp wold be broken, and the expedition would head into the little-known land to the west. Somewhere out there was the Mexican boundary. Nobody knew exactly where. The Indians still thought that the land was theirs. But who cared what an Indian thought?

Curious townspeople gathered about the camp. They were curious because there was an air of mystery about the undertaking. Captain Becknell had advertised for "a company of men destined to the Westward for the purpose of trading for Horses and Mules, and catching wild animals of every description." Nobody believed that this was the truth; at least, not the whole truth. The town marshal was questioning a tall, blue-eyed, tight-lipped individual known as Trapper Jim in the hope of finding out something.

"How come you signed on with Cap Becknell, Jim?"

The trapper looked up from cleaning his gun. "Why not? He's a good man."

"I thought you was an engagé," said the marshal. "Didn't you work for the Hudson's Bay Company? Or was it for Mr. John Jacob Astor?"

Trapper Jim shook his head. "I been a freeman these two years."

(A hunter or trapper who worked for the great fur companies was called an "engagé." When he cut loose and went out for himself, he was a "freeman.")

"I guess you're hunting more than beaver this trip," the marshal said with a wink.

Trapper Jim looked innocent. "Prime skins are fetching six dollars apiece," he said.

"Gold's fetching more than that. Ever hear of the Seven Lost Cities of Cibola?"

The trapper smiled. "Everybody's heard of Cibola."

"And you don't believe there's gold there?"

"Trail-talk," said Trapper Jim.

"I reckon you don't believe in Santa Fe, either."

"Oh, certainly—sure! Captain Becknell's been there."

An old fellow with one arm thrust his gray head forward. He had lost the other arm from a poison-arrow wound in the Shoshone country. That is probably why he was called "Indian Isaacs." He called, "You headed for Santa Fe? They'll throw you in jail."

"Not me," said Trapper Jim. "I don't want any Mexicanos. I'll do my trading with the Indians."

"Arrows for bullets. That's the kind of trade you'll get," the old man said sourly.

"Don't worry," the marshal said. "They'll never get as far as the bad Indian country. Not with those wagons."

A pudgy little teamster broke in, addressing Trapper Jim excitedly. "You ain't figurin' on takin' *wagons* on the trail!"

"That's the notion," the other replied.

"There's never been a wagon-train west of the Big Muddy,"—the Missouri River—the little man said, "and there never will be. Cap Becknell must be loco."

He proceeded to list the many reasons why a wheeled vehicle could not go through. Between the Big Muddy and the Rocky Mountains were many water-courses, large and small. In all that six hundred miles there was neither bridge nor ferry. There were fords, it is true, but these were covered by rushing water during the flood season. Mules and horses could swim. Could a heavy "Pittsburgh" swim loaded with two tons of trade? How could they get their loads up and down the steep banks of the river-bottoms?

The little man hadn't finished yet. What did they know about the swamps that lined the rivers? Had they had any experience of quicksands? Suppose they did reach the foothills. The passes were choked with boulders as big as houses; you had to unpack your critter to get him through.

And look what a temptation a wagon-train would be to prowling Indians! No, no! They'd never make it. Of that the pudgy little teamster was sure. They'd lose their wagons and probably their scalps.

It was a strange group that milled about in the camp. Only one man of the thirty besides the Captain was forty years old. This was Harmon Gregg, who had had experience with mule-trains and the slower ox-trains from the East. Ewing Young and Joseph R. Walker had taken the Santa Fe trip of the previous year.

William Wolfskill, a gently bred Kentuckian of twenty-four, had joined because he had heard golden tales of the Far West. He was looking for a place to his liking where he could settle down and make a homestead. He was a dead shot and would be useful both on the game-trail and in case of Indian trouble.

Of the others, a dozen were mountain men like Trapper Jim, as many more were teamsters and mule-wranglers. A couple, in cloth instead of leather jackets and with bright neckerchiefs, looked as if they might be gamblers. Another pair were rivermen who had tired of the Mississippi trade. The remainder were the hopeful, restless, take-a-chance type of young men who were pushing American civilization ever farther toward the Pacific.

Treasure or trade or just travel, it was all one to them, provided there were adventure and novelty.

Two half-breeds in the center of the camp were about to give an exhibition of how to pack a mule. Captain Becknell had ordered this for the benefit of the inexperienced members. He now came out of his tent to oversee the work. He addressed the taller of the men as *cargador*. The language of mule packing was largely Spanish.

"There's no slicker pair of *arrieros* (packers) on the plains than these two," Captain Becknell explained. "They can pack a *mula de carga* so slick he don't hardly know he's loaded, and do it in five minutes. Go it, *hombres!*"

Strewn about on the ground were small packets of cloth, utensils, and knick-knacks. These would make up the load of three hundred pounds, which was the most that a mule would carry. It must be evenly balanced, too. The mule knew as much about it as the men. If the burden were not properly adjusted, the animal would roll its eyes and grumble. If it was still dissatisfied, it would kick. Finally it would lie down and roll. There was no answer to that argument.

The *cargador* and his assistant now set to work. A square pad of raw sheepskin, rubbed and pounded to softness and stuffed with hay, was

first thrown across the mule's broad back for a foundation. "That's the *salea*," Captain Becknell announced. "That's to prevent the critter's hide from chafing. Next, the *xerga*."

The saddlecloth was swiftly and neatly adjusted, the partners working with smooth skill, one on either side of the animal. The *cargador*, on the left, swung the heavy saddle into place and set it carefully.

"There goes the *aparejo*," the Captain said. "Watch 'em, boys, how they fix it. You can ruin a hundred dollars' worth of mule by bad saddling."

Strong, wide bandages of woven grass, passed in and out and over in an intricate pattern, bound the saddle into place. As the husky *arrieros* hauled the cinch-bands tight, the mule set to grunting and groaning in protest.

"Ouch!" exclaimed the voice of a sympathetic onlooker.

The *cargador* looked up with a twinkle. "Don't you never believe a word a mule says," he said.

The Captain bore him out. "That mule ain't sufferin' none. But he would, if the *aparejo* wasn't cinched up good and tight. A couple of hours out on the trail and it would fetch lose and start to rub and the poor critter's back would be raw meat. He don't know what's good for him, that's all."

The cargo bags were now slung across the

sturdy back. The two workers proceeded to fill them with such regularity of movement that they seemed like twin machines. The weight was kept as near even as possible.

Presently the animal showed signs of restiveness. The *cargador* spoke soothingly to him, but he began to jig on his feet. The man looked around and spoke a single, sharp word:

"*Tapajos!*"

From the crowd a leather strap was handed to him. He slipped it upon the mule's head, covering the nervously rolling eyes. Immediately the mule became perfectly quiet.

"Remember that, boys," the Captain told the attentive circle. "Blindfold a mule, and he'll stand like a lamb."

The work of loading was now completed. Picking up a long rope, the *cargador*, with the help of the other *arriero*, took several swift, accurate turns about the pack and beneath the animal's belly. At the end he set his knee in the ribs for a purchase and gave a final, mighty heave, to which the mule responded with a plaintive gurgle.

The load was now safely set. A deft turn of the end knotted it in place. The helper whisked away the *tapajos,* and the mule turned his head to look over his load.

"*Adios!*" the *cargador* cried. This was a signal to the man opposite.

"*Vaya!*" the assistant replied, meaning that all was in order on his side.

"*Anda!*" the *cargador* snapped and gave the mule a friendly whack over the rump.

The animal trotted contentedly off. The lesson was over.

Trapper Jim and half of the others went into town to make their final purchases. Franklin was a flourishing settlement of perhaps five hundred inhabitants crowded into a little more than one hundred single-story log cabins. There were a dozen stores, four taverns, a jail, and a post office. Slow ox-carts brought in goods from the East. Flatboats, carrying merchandise, worked their way one hundred and fifty miles up-current from St. Louis, with its population of nearly five thousand. Much of this trade would be transferred to

the pack trains. For Franklin was then the outpost
of trade. Four years later it was nothing. The
river had swept it away.

On the way back, Trapper Jim passed the
town marshal. Reining in his mustang, the official
shouted a farewell.

"If you find Cibola, bring me back a set of gold
buttons for my pants!" he called, and laughed.

5

All Set!

DAYBREAK WAS THE SIGNAL FOR CAMPBREAK. This was a sort of game, for each pair of travelers tried to be ready first. The members worked in pairs, both with pack-mule and wagon. Several old-timers among the number set the pace.

As soon as the few cooking utensils were

packed and the fires were put out by the *madre* (Spanish for mother, the trail-name for the cook), the trail captain took charge. Ewing Young had been elected to that office the night before. Satisfying himself that all was in order, he lifted his arm.

"Ready?" he called.

The men stood alert. "Ready." "Ready." "All ready." The answers came back from all sides.

Down came the arm. "Catch up!" the trail captain shouted.

This was the signal for a race. Every wagon crew, every pack outfit, strove for the honor of being first prepared for the trail. Packs were cinched down tight. Wagonloads were settled in. Horses took their places at the wagon tongues. Presently there came a triumphant call.

"All set!"

A brisk pair had finished in the lead.

"Take your place forward."

The winning pair led their mule to the lead of the line.

Now the call was repeated from all sides: "All set, here!" "All set!" "All set!" as the line formed.

Trail Captain Ewing Young took in the whole setup with a keen eye and gave the signal:

"Fall in."

The wagons settled into order, two by two. The mules and spare horses stepped to their marching positions.

"Stretch out!" ordered the captain.

"Hep!" the muleteers snapped.

"Giddap!" the wagoners commanded.

"Hold your line," Ewing Young directed.

They straggled irregularly out on the prairie. Now that the race was over, the men went slack. From his saddle, Captain Becknell looked them over with a critical eye. He hummed a line from an old song, "The Raggle-taggle Gyps-eye-O!"

Riding beside him, Harmon Gregg grinned. "Don't think much of your outfit, eh?"

"Too early to tell," the leader said.

A voice was raised in song:

> *"We're on our way
> To Santa Fe."*

The musical muleteer interrupted himself to shout a question across to Becknell. "How far you reckon it is, Cap?" he asked earnestly.

"A thousand miles, might be," the leader answered.

"Little short of it if anything," Ewing Young amended.

"My mule can do that on his hind legs," the man boasted.

"How long are you figuring for the trip?" Gregg asked.

"Tell you better in a week. No wagon's ever tried it before."

"Three-four months?" the other persisted.

"If the luck is with us," was the best that the questioner could get out of Becknell.

The organization was loosely military. At the same meeting of all members which picked Ewing Young as trail captain, Joseph R. Walker was elected camp captain. These two would divide the command and the responsibilities of the march.

Walker had had wide experience in the field. He knew where the water was good, where it was too salty to drink, and where it was so mineralized as to be dangerous. Private maps of his own making told where there was softwood for fires and hardwood to mend broken axles or wheel-spokes. He was familiar with the richest grazing grounds. If he passed up some likely looking camp site, it was because of the mosquitoes or buffalo gnats which would have tortured man and beast. A night's sleep is a necessity on the trail.

As soon as camp was pitched at the end of a day, the life and comfort of every creature became Walker's responsibility. He oversaw the turning out of the animals to graze. If he thought it necessary to guard the camp at night, he could place sentries. He inspected animals for lameness or disease, and wagons for damage. His was a hard life from sunset to sunrise. The rest of the time he could crawl into a wagon and go to sleep.

Where the camp captain left off, the trailmaster took over. It was his duty to select the easiest route for travel. He was responsible for the safety of the caravan on the march. He sent out scouts to watch for Indians and game. If a river was to be crossed, he would decide upon the safest ford and make sure that there were no quicksands to swallow up animals and wagons. This was not easy. Often the stream-bottoms shifted, and a crossing which had been safe one week might be dangerous the next.

A good trail captain possessed an instinctive sense of the lay of the land. Ewing Young was a good trail captain. Like Walker, he was a hunter and trapper of experience. The two men worked well together.

How far their authority could extend depended largely upon their characters. Every member of the *atajo*, when he signed on in the expedition book, had agreed to obey the orders of the duly elected officers. But he was not likely to take this seriously. Except in time of emergency, such as attack by Indians, every man would tend to act as if he were his own boss. He might or might not take orders from the captains.

Back of the two was the power and reputation of Captain William Becknell. He had not been elected to any office. But it was understood that his was the final authority in a crisis. It was also understood, by those who knew him, that he would never interfere with his lieutenants unless absolutely necessary.

"Don't come to me with anything you can handle yourselves," he warned them.

The second night out, there was a minor test. They were making only fair time, considering that the course was all flat, easy country, and had come in late to a good camping spot called the Glen. Here, after sniffing at the air and testing the wind with wet forefinger, Walker blew his whistle for attention and gave an unpopular order:

"Spades and shovels!"

This meant that all packs must be got under cover and drainage ditches dug to carry off surface water. Objections were raised at once.

"Who says it's goin' to rain?" "Look at them stars, shinin' bright." "Wind's in a clear quarter." "I'll take a chance."

Trapper Jim, Pete, the *madre*, and several others got out tools and did their ditching. The rest turned in. The camp master did not press his order. It was too soon to risk trouble. Let them learn by experience.

Early the next morning the wind shifted, the clouds gathered, and there was a great downpour of rain. Too late, the men who had refused to obey staggered out and did what they could to protect their merchandise. Several of the packs were soaked. The owners were obliged to unpack and spread the cloth in the sun. It was a mean job and delayed the whole caravan.

Harmon Gregg reported to the camp master what he had overheard one of the luckless mule-men say to his fellow: "I reckon that Walker *hombre's* got more in his *cabeza* than we thought." It was the first lesson, but it was not enough.

6

The First Test

AFTER THAT, IT WAS ALL EASY GOING FOR A
week. As the process of making and breaking
camp became more familiar, the *atajo* was able to
make good time. Fifteen, seventeen, even twenty
miles a day was not too much over the pleasant,
grassy flats.

The greenhorns thought it was going to be like that all the way. They were living well on wild turkey, wild pigeon, and antelope meat, and liking it. Most of the streams harbored fish. Life was pleasant, and the men fell readily into the simple routine of camp, inevitably growing slack as pleasant day followed pleasant day.

The animals did not share the slackness. After the third day out, every mule knew his proper place in line. At the word of command, they fell in like soldiers. Any animal who attempted to crowd was admonished by a swift kick in the ribs to stay where he belonged. Captain Becknell observed somewhat grimly:

"The critters have got more gumption than the men."

They had been out ten days when, one bright morning, everything started wrong. Two pack animals got into a quarrel over position, and a wrangler was severely bitten trying to pacify them. When they were quieted, the bell-mare could not be found. The mules would not move without her. She was their leader. Mules are that way; nobody knows why. The annoyed Ewing

Young found the mare cooling her feet in a pool and looking at the scenery. When she was led back, one mule decided to lie down and roll, dislocating his pack. The load had to be taken off and repacked, to the exasperation of the two muleteers.

A valuable hour was wasted before they took the trail. Just as the call for noon stop was sounded, a wheel on Trapper Jim's wagon changed its shape from round to oval. Some of the spokes had weakened; the wheel was "sprung" and useless. An extra half-hour was lost while that was being repaired.

At a small creek crossing, the men were set upon by a cloud of green deer-flies which drew blood at every attack. Everyone was out of temper by mid-afternoon, when the sky clouded and a drizzle set in. The trail captain looked up at Leader Becknell.

"If we don't make Rock Creek, we'll be in trouble."

"Make it, then," Captain Becknell said.

"We can't get there before sundown."

Becknell nodded. "Then we'll get there after. Shake 'em up a bit."

The men responded with ill humor to the speed-up. Lanterns were out before the ripples of the rising waters of Rock Creek warned them. The tired men and animals began to spread.

"Hold your ranks," the trail captain called sharply.

Mutterings and protests rose. "Ain't we going to camp?" "What about grub?" "I'm clean tuckered, and my livestock is worse."

"We've got to cross that water now," Ewing Young said positively.

"Why?" The question came from several quarters in tones ranging from challenge to plaintiveness.

"It'll be worse in the morning," Young said.

"And if we wait till then, we'll start cold-collar," a wagoner backed him up. He meant that a draught-animal sets out in the morning with muscles chilled and stiff and works up to the strain. Not until it gets "hot under the collar" can it meet a severe test.

"That's right," the *madre* said. "Never stop the night on the near side of rising water."

A former ox-team driver from the East said sulkily, "I call for a vote."

"Vote on the other side," the trail captain said. "Come on, boys."

"He's got a right to a vote," one of the flashily dressed gamblers put in.

"Anybody's got a right to a vote," Young conceded, "but this isn't the time for it."

"My wagon stops here," the ox-man declared. Several voices supported him. "No vote, no move." "The critters is wore out." "I don't go where I can't see." "Wait till morning."

Captain Becknell advanced to the front. He held a lantern high. "There'll be no vote," he said. "This *atajo* crosses. Follow me."

There was an uncertain moment. Then Trapper Jim urged his horses forward into the black current.

Two of the three other wagons followed. A handful of those who had raised rebellious voices unhitched.

With Captain Becknell, Young, and Walker

guiding, the train stumbled and splashed across without mishap.

In the morning the trail leader's foresight was proven. Swollen with all-night rains, the stream had become a foaming torrent.

On the far bank one of the mutineers was waving and shouting, "Captain Becknell, Captain Becknell, what'll we do? What'll we *do?*"

The leader glanced at the seething flood. No wagon could live in it for ten seconds. He cupped his hands at his mouth and shouted back, "Go home and paint your nose blue!"

Ewing Young said to Gregg under his breath, "There'll be trouble before we get some of these colts broke in."

7

Indian Trade

THE PACE SLOWED DOWN. WHAT WAS THE hurry, the men asked themselves. It was pleasant enough making ten or twelve miles a day across the richly grassed plains, with two hours at noon to rest the men and feed the animals.

It was less pleasant crossing the many watercourses which cut through the land. Some were easy to ford. Others might cost weary miles of detour. Often the banks were steep and dangerous. At Stranger Creek in Kansas a sudden landslide, started by a struggling mule, buried a packhorse below. Before they could dig him out of the rubble, he was dead.

On the tenth day out, they came to a rough signboard on the brink of a small stream. It was at a fork of the trail and pointed northwest. Any evidence that white men had traveled that way before was a matter of lively interest. The travelers gathered around to read.

```
┌──────────────┐
│   OREGON     │
│   TRAIL      │
└──────────────┘
```

"That's a small signpost for a big country," Harmon Gregg remarked.

"It's the biggest country in the world, I reckon," Trapper Jim said.

"Ever been up that trail?" one of the rivermen asked.

Jim nodded. "I've had all of it that I want."

"Is it tougher than this?" one of the new men inquired.

The trapper stared at him. "This? Call this hard? Why, it's as safe as your granny's kitchen beside that north country. Half of the men that go in up there never come out."

A discontented voice said, "*We* ain't out yet. I don't believe the Old Man knows where he is right now. Always studyin' over them old maps of his."

"Why don't you ask him?" Gregg suggested.

"You reckon he'd tell me?"

"Well," said Gregg with a thoughtful air, "he might. And then again, he mightn't. But if I was going to ask sassy questions of the boss, I'd put a brick in the seat of my pants first."

"We got a right to know where we're going, ain't we?" a mule-man said.

"We're going to Council Grove," Ewing Young volunteered.

"Where's that?"

"At the plumb end of nowhere," the trailmaster replied with a grin.

"Well, I don't like it and I wish I had my ten

dollars back," one of the rivermen declared, and there were mutterings of assent.

Gregg reported the spirit of possible mischief to his chief.

"Let 'em chatter," Captain Becknell said. "It'll ease their tempers."

For some time he had felt that they were forgetting the lesson of discipline learned by the experience at the ford. When they should reach "bad" country, the members would have to live up to their promises and obey orders without question. Captain Becknell was an experienced and patient man, dealing with inexperienced and impatient men. He would bide his time.

Two days of steady rain lowered the spirits of the travelers. At One-Hundred-and-Ten Mile Creek they lost a day waiting for the water to go down, and nearly lost a wagon because the driver did not want to wait. At a smaller, nameless rivulet, another wagon stuck in the mud so firmly that it took half the mules in camp to haul it out. The men continued to mutter that it was a fool trick to try wheeled traffic in that country, anyway.

"You haven't seen anything yet," Harmon Gregg, the old trail hand, told them grimly. "Wait till we hit the mountains."

The trail was still well to the north of the Arkansas River, still in rich country. There would always be water, wood, and forage there for the animals. But there were places where only an experienced frontiersman could find the short cuts across country which would save many miles. Rain had washed out the hoof marks of the few previous expeditions. The trailmaster here must pick his own way.

Scouting ahead of the slow-moving train soon after the morning start, one of the hunters noticed a forked stick planted in the ground. In the fork was wedged a small square of paper, protected from the weather by a fold of bark. There was no writing on the paper; only a crude picture of a human form and below it a rough design of uncertain outline. The hunter galloped in and the experts gathered around interestedly to interpret it.

"It's a message from some trapper who doesn't know how to write," Ewing Young said.

Harmon Gregg studied the bark. "Hasn't been here more than two-three days," he said.

Captain Becknell glanced at the human figure. "Indians around. He's telling us."

"Friendly Indians," Joe Walker said, pointing to the penciled outline.

"How'd you figger that?" a muleteer asked.

"That's a pipe he's drawn," the plainsman replied. "If they'd been hostile, he'd have drawn an arrow."

"Anyway, we'll keep a watch out," the trail captain decided.

He sent out four riders with orders not to stray more than a mile or two from the caravan. Toward sunset a shot was heard and a youth who went by the name of Ohio Slim came galloping in.

"Injuns! Injuns!" he shouted. "They're on the warpath."

"Where and how many?" Ewing Young inquired coolly.

"Out there," the scared young man babbled excitedly. "Hundreds of 'em. They've got their squaws and papooses with 'em."

"Then they're not on the warpath," the trail captain said. "Calm down. Indians never take their families into a fight. We'll look."

Captain Becknell joined him, and the two disappeared across a rise. From its top they sighted a band of perhaps two dozen Osages. Their head man, riding out, made the sign of peace, to which the white leader responded. The two men met on a grassy hillock and dismounted. They exchanged remarks in the two-handed sign language, to this general effect:

"We wish to trade with the white men," from the Indian.

"We have goods to trade with you," from the white man.

The Osage drew out a pipe. The caravan leader produced his pipe. Tobacco was exchanged. A squaw brought fire in an earthware bowl.

Both men squatted on the ground and lighted up. Drawing in a draught that swelled his scrawny cheeks, the Osage breathed a cloud downward. Captain Becknell followed suit. One puff for earth. Indian and white man now pointed their noses heavenward and *whoofed* their mouthfuls of smoke into the air. One puff for the skies. Twice more they sucked in and vigorously discharged the blasts of vapor, east and west. One puff each for air and water. The ceremonial was over. They were ready to trade.

The whole band headed for the train, which had halted. Captain Becknell shouted a warning in English which the savages did not understand.

"Watch out for 'em. They'll steal the shine off a brass button."

Braves and squaws mixed with the whites. The braves wanted powder and tobacco. The women begged for beads and trinkets. But they had little to offer in return. Their beaver furs were thin. The buffalo robes were ill-cured and mangy.

When the Indians found that they could do no more business with the palefaces, they tried to pick up odd objects, only to be cracked over the knuckles by the watchful whites. They took it in good part. It was a sort of game with them. There was nothing wrong in stealing if you could get away with it. If you were caught, you made no fuss but hoped for better luck next time. That was the Indian code of morals.

Two days later, the *atajo* met with another band. This was a smaller group, traveling eastward and making good time. No women or children were with them, but they, too, wished to trade, not to fight. They knew one white man's word. It was "swap." They looked greedily at the wagons and repeated in Spanish and Yankee, "*Para* swap. *Para* swap."

Very well, the whites were willing. But what did the Indians have? Pete, the *madre*, acting as interpreter, made the animal sign. Did they have furs? No; no furs. Gold, then? No, the Indians had no gold. Turquoises? Shiny stones, meaning desert "emeralds"? It was not likely that the tribes this far east would have any of these valuables. Still, it was always worth trying. But no, the Indians had nothing.

They did produce some trail food: dried pumpkin, maize, beans. Becknell's men, who were traveling light in the matter of food, were glad to get the vegetables. Some cases were opened up, and the trade proceeded satisfactorily for both sides. Cheap cotton goods and bright buttons were exchanged for the food supplies. When there was no more business to be done, the little band melted away without a word. Indians never said good-bye. They just left.

As they vanished over a distant rise, one of the whites had a belated idea.

"Why didn't we ask 'em if they saw any buf-falo?"

Joe Walker grinned. "Save your wind. They'd never tell you if they did."

8

Buffalo!

ALWAYS ALERT FOR SIGNS, JOE WALKER, THE
camp captain, addressed his companions at breakfast.

"Anybody hear those coyotes last night?"

A mule-man said, "Sounded hungry."

"That wasn't the hunger cry," the experienced camp master said. "They were feeding."

"What on, would you think?" Ewing Young asked.

"Might be dead buffalo," Walker replied.

"Where there's dead buffalo, there's live buffalo," Captain Becknell said.

Pete, the cook, smacked his lips loudly. "I'd admire to have prairie beef for dinner," he said.

"Suppose you ride wide tomorrow, Jim," the trail captain addressed the tall, blue-eyed trapper. "We could lay off for a day's hunting."

Their course was now leading southwest toward Council Grove. They were in buffalo country, the heavy, rich grassland of the prairies, but saw no sign of the huge animals. Toward the middle of the afternoon, a trapper who had been scouting forward appeared on the crest of a distant ridge.

His bronco was galloping at full speed. The rider was flailing his arms and yelling. When he came within earshot, they could make out the words, "Buffaloes! Buffaloes! They're after me."

The wagons drew close together. Soon there loomed against the horizon the dark line of massed bodies. Heads down, the buffalo were plunging blindly ahead. It was a stampede.

The frightened rider drew in his horse back of the nearest wagon. He begged the men to get out their guns and check the charging bisons while there was time. Captain Becknell tried to calm him down.

"Don't fluster yourself," he advised. "They'll never overrun the wagons."

Sure enough, the herd swerved sharply to the right and thundered on. Instantly the men of the *atajo* got their guns out, spurred their horses and mules to the chase, and shot down the helpless prey point-blank. There was no resistance. It was sheer slaughter. Bulls, cows, and calves, a score of them lay bleeding on the ground. It was the custom of the day, which was to continue through the years until the species was almost wiped out. Today only a few remain. These are cared for in semi-captivity.

Trapper Jim rode in and looked about at the dead, dying, and wounded creatures in disgust.

"Now you've killed 'em, what are you going to do with 'em?" he asked one of the hunters who was going from body to body, cutting out the tongues.

"Eat 'em," the man said, with a grin.

"This whole *atajo* couldn't eat one buffalo," the trapper retorted. "Better save powder and ball for the time when you may need 'em."

"Prairie beef" was good eating. The big hump supplied rich, suety meat. The bones, cracked open, yielded a marrow which was prepared as "prairie butter." Ribs and loin were preferred by many plainsmen to the best elk, antelope, or deer venison. There was a mighty feast that evening when the halt for camp was called. There was also unwelcome news.

"We'll form corral for the night," Camp Captain Walker announced.

This meant added work. The wagons would be drawn up to form a hollow square. All draft animals would be hobbled before being turned out to graze, foreleg closely bound to foreleg with stout straps. This prevented their wandering far. In case of attack, they would be hustled inside the enclosure where they could not be run off by marauding savages.

The overfed and sleepy caravan men saw no need for all that trouble. Mutters of discontent were heard.

"What does Walker want to get so notional about Indians for?" somebody asked.

"No bad Indians east of Council Grove," another said. "Every fool knows that."

"I'm tired of being bossed around," a third said, and a companion backed him up with, "Might as well be in the Army."

The campmaster turned on him. "Maybe you think those buffaloes were running for exercise," he said mildly.

"That was a stampede," Trapper Jim put in. "They were good and scared."

"What scairt 'em?" one of the objectors asked.

"Well, it wasn't no prairie dog," the cook said. "It might be Injuns or it might not."

"And they might be good Injuns or they might be bad," the trapper remarked.

"The sooner you get the corral shaped up, the

quicker you'll get to sleep," the campmaster pointed out.

The weary men got the wagons into position and the animals outside. Rifles, flints, powder, and bullets were made ready. Grumbling, the members performed their tasks and prepared to turn in when they got a second and worse shock.

"We'll set guard tonight," the campmaster announced.

An immediate outcry arose. It was all foolishness. The camp dogs would give the alarm if anything stirred. The men wanted their sleep.

"Orders," Walker said curtly.

The night was to be divided into three watches: nine to twelve, twelve to three, three to six. The men could draw lots for it. Or they could play euchre or poker or seven-up. But however they decided it, four men must be constantly on post, one to each corner, a hundred yards out.

The idea of gambling for it pleased them. The winners escaped duty for the night. The second lot had first choice and always took the early watch. To be routed out of warm blankets into the chill prairie air, part way through the night, was no man's choice. All grumbled. There was nothing unusual in that. Men on the trail always grumbled. It was their way of letting off steam.

But, in the end, Becknell's men, though they might be slack about it, found it wise to obey orders.

9
Watch Out!

YEARS OF HARSH TRAINING ON THE FUR TRAILS
of the North had accustomed Trapper Jim to
discipline. There men had to hang together. They
had to consider their own wishes less important
than the good of the band, if they were to go on
living. Trapper Jim was ready at all times to back

the chosen officers of the *atajo*. But he had his private opinion of the new hard routine. He spoke to Harmon Gregg aside.

"Is the Old Man really worried about Injuns?"

"Cap Becknell? Not yet," the other said.

"Then what's all the fahdoodle about?" Trapper Jim asked.

"He wants to get the boys used to taking orders," Gregg replied.

"It won't hurt 'em, I guess," the trapper said. "They've got plenty to learn."

After a few nights of the routine, Walker became suspicious that the sentries were not attending to business. His opportunity to teach them a lesson came when camp was pitched on the edge of a cottonwood grove. Sometime in the early morning, the camp was invaded and a twenty-five pound sack of bacon stolen, together with a batch of Pete's rock-like camp bread.

Trained in woodcraft, Walker was able to identify the thieves by certain marks. Two large bobcats had sneaked into camp and helped themselves. It put an idea into the shrewd head of the camp captain. He carefully erased all signs of the

thieves. At the breakfast fire he called for attention.

"This camp was robbed last night."

There was a chorus of surprise and disbelief.

"Who was on the late watch?" Walker asked.

Four of the men spoke up. Each one was sure
that no Indians could have sneaked past him.
(Walker had said nothing about Indians, but this
was what he wished them to believe.) The most
voluble was young Ohio Slim.

"I never closed an eye the whole three hours,"
he declared virtuously.

The day before Ohio Slim had been heard to
remark that a fellow could get just as good sleep
out on the pee-rary as he could in camp, if he
knew how to fix things. Walker knew this, but
he kept it to himself.

From then on, he had an eye out for the youth.
The next night Slim had the midnight watch. His
station was near a copse of black locust. He went
to it whistling and trying to conceal the fact that
he had wrapped a warm blanket around his body.

At two o'clock in the morning the moon had
sunk below the horizon. A soft wind rustled the

tall prairie grasses. From the thicket a dim figure stepped forth. It dropped to all fours, then went flat on its belly. Swiftly it snaked its way toward the sentry at that corner. The sentry did not notice it. The sentry did not notice anything. He was deep in the enjoyment of a refreshing nap.

The prowling figure rose and leapt.

Wild clamor broke out. Dogs barked. Rudely awakened sleepers shouted. Grazing animals snorted and plunged. Men seized their guns and ran out. In the half-light they saw a horrid figure. It looked human, but seemed to have no head. It stumbled around in little circles, uttering muffled yelps. The authoritative voice of Joe Walker called:

"Muzzles down! Don't shoot."

He seized the strange figure and propelled it toward the corral. From it came a string of muffled curses and threats.

"Lights," Walker ordered.

A lantern was brought. The camp captain whipped a flour-bag off his captive's head and shoulders, and addressed him.

"What if I had been an Indian, Slim?"

The youth spit and spluttered like an enraged bobcat.

"You were asleep," the captain charged.

"I was not!"

"You were so sound asleep that you didn't even feel me pulling that flour-bag down over your head."

"Dirty trick," Slim muttered.

"Or snugging it in close with my lasso," Walker continued.

"I mighta shut my eyes for a minute," the young man admitted. "But that don't——"

"Then you own up to falling asleep on post," the campmaster broke in.

"Maybe I did for a minute," the youth said sullenly. "What of it?"

"Three dollars; that's what of it," Walker snapped. "You're fined three dollars for endangering the safety of the outfit."

The offender paid up. He got off easy. In some *atajos* he would have been flogged.

The lesson of discipline, begun by Captain Becknell at the flooded ford, was being driven home.

10

Men of Peace

SMALL ALARMS KEPT THE TRAVELERS ON THE
alert for a time. Two horsemen, sighted against
the distant sky, started a report of Indian war
parties nearby. A sudden night panic among the
animals, with no apparent cause, woke up the entire caravan to warlike activity. Every wagon

bristled with guns. Rifles were fired at shadows. But nothing happened. The result was that the groundless scares left the men more careless than before.

Riding as outpost one cloudy day, Ohio Slim hurried back with a report of something queer going on in a steep cleft between rocky hills near the river. He had seen a wisp of smoke and dimly heard strange noises. It must be a war-song, he thought, for who but redskins would be making music in that wilderness?

Trapper Jim volunteered to investigate. He saddled his trotting mule and rode out. Two hundred yards from the edge of the rocky defile he dismounted and let the reins fall over the animal's head to the ground. The mule stood as if hitched to an invisible rail. Trail animals were trained to do that. Flattened in the grass, the investigator crept forward. He peered cautiously over the brink and at the sight below him, gave a chuckle of relief.

Two tattered figures were crouched before a feeble fire. A very small fish was spitted over the flame. One of them lifted it off, placed it on a

flat rock for a dish, and divided it accurately with
his knife. Both kneeled and asked a blessing on
the food. By this, the watcher above knew them
to be missionaries. The "war-song" heard by the
alarmed outpost was a Baptist hymn.

Waiting until they had finished their scanty
meal, Trapper Jim hailed the men and told them
of the approaching wagon train. They were trail-
wise and advised that the caravan leave the uplands and travel along the river bottom, where
low water made the going easy. They had been
out for six months, converting such Indians as
they met, they said, and were now on their way
to Council Grove. The trapper looked at them in
astonishment.

"Where are your animals?" he asked.

"Grizzlies killed them. Back in the mountains."

"And you haven't any guns?"

"No," they said. If they traveled armed, the
Indians would not believe in their good faith.

"Come back and see the boss," Trapper Jim
invited.

He led them to Captain Becknell, who questioned them about the country. They were piti-

fully thin. Their clothes were rags. Their boots clung to their feet only because they were cross-bound like pack-saddles with cloth strips and twine. The knapsacks in which they carried their supplies were as thin as they were.

"Isn't there something you need?" Captain Becknell asked.

They looked at one another sorrowfully. "We haven't any trade," the larger one said. A dozen small otter skins made up their stock. They were mangy and poor, for the summer pelts of fur-bearing animals are almost worthless. If they could be exchanged for a shilling's worth of goods at the distant trading post, the owners would be lucky.

Captain Becknell would not even examine them. "I don't ask trade of God's men," he said. "Tell me what you want."

With some difficulty, he argued the grateful missionaries into accepting a small quantity of the articles they most sorely needed. They took a little salt, a little sugar, a few strips of bacon, a bag of crackers, a spool of coarse packthread and some oil for their cracked boots. Then they went on their way, leaving their thanks and blessings behind them.

"That ought to bring us good luck," the Captain said to the trailmaster.

The meeting with the missionaries had an unexpected result. Some men had been unhappy under the Becknell system. There had been no trouble with the savages. They had seen hardly any, just a few bands too small to be dangerous. What was the use of all this fuss and bother about forming corral every night? They were good and tired of mounting guard and losing their sleep. There were no hostile tribes near. It was the same old argument, but backed up now by the case of the missionaries. If two unarmed men could travel for months in safety, didn't that prove the uselessness of keeping up such a strict guard?

The rebels got together and chose an ex-gambler, Faro Mike, as their spokesman. He was a slick-tongued fellow who had been on the stage and boasted that he was "a fast crab with my clacker." He politely requested a hearing from

Captain Becknell. The leader invited Harmon Gregg, Joseph Walker, and Ewing Young to sit in.

Fargo Mike opened the talk. "We want a trail-vote."

"Who's we?" Captain Becknell asked.

The gambler was ready for that. "Here's the list," he said. He held out a sheet of paper. Several of the signers had written their names. More were in Mike's own handwriting with the sign "X, his mark," by those who could not write. Captain Becknell ran his eye down the list.

"Thirteen names," he said. "Might be bad luck," and he grinned.

"We want a vote," the spokesman repeated.

"You got a right to it," the leader admitted. "What on?"

"This night business."

"You want a loose camp?" Walker struck in. "All spread out where Indians can rush us one by one?"

"Well, no," the gambler said. "We're willing to make corral in reason. But not all this sentry-go business."

"Call the meeting," Becknell told the camp-master.

Every man dropped what he was doing and gathered at the dying fire. Faro Mike delivered a speech. Captain Becknell might mean well, he said, but he was pushing things too far. Men couldn't ride hard all day and then sit up half the night on watch. It wasn't reasonable. The country was quiet. All the Indians they had seen were peaceful. Peaceful? They were plumb scared —no danger from them. And so on and so forth.

In reply Captain Becknell said briefly that some people never believed in danger until it was too late. For himself, he'd rather lose his sleep than his scalp. Those who felt differently could vote as they thought best.

Pete, the *madre*, addressed Faro Mike: "You won't talk so bunkum when you wake up some morning with an arrow through your gizzard."

"Clam it!" the gambler retorted. "I wasn't born in the woods to be scared by an owl."

The vote was taken. Captain Becknell's party was outvoted by five ballots.

"All right," the leader said. "Those that don't

want to stand guard, needn't. I'll take a post every night. Who's with me?"

The officials, including Pete, promptly volunteered, as did Trapper Jim and William Wolfskill. Three of the hunters followed suit. So did the young Ohioan. He had had his lesson. It meant a hard and grueling test for the willing ones. Pete turned upon the gambler's supporters.

"Maybe you think I like ridin' herd on you," he said. "A bunch of doodlers and inglers and bounetters, that's what you are. Anybody want to fight on that? No! Well, sweet dreams."

11

Good-bye, Civilization

Four weeks' travel brought them in sight
of Council Grove. It was nothing much to look
at; one trading post and a couple of log buildings.
One of them was for animals, the other for
humans. There was little difference. The advantage, if any, was with the stable.

The *atajo* had come almost 350 miles. All things considered, Captain Becknell was fairly satisfied with their progress. A pack-train would have made better time. But then a pack-train would have had fewer difficulties of traffic to face. Hoofs could carry animals where wheels could not carry heavy loads.

Loss of time did not worry the leader. He was not especially interested in making a quick journey. What he was out for was to prove that wagons could do what everybody said they could not do —reach Santa Fe. If they could, there would be a big trade rolling southwest.

Thus far the expedition had been, in a sense, within the borders of civilization. Civilization ended at Council Grove. This was the last settlement of white men, the final trading-post. West of it, a straight line of travel would bring them to the Great Bend of the Arkansas River. But it was always a question how straight a line could be made. Indians, washouts, or prairie fires might compel the expedition to make detours.

Once they had reached the river they could follow its course up into the mountains and turn

south through the high passes to another and older civilization in Mexico. No trouble about that. The river marked the trail for those who had gone before. Captain Becknell had other ideas, but he was keeping them to himself until later.

West of Council Grove stretched the wilderness. Entering it, they would be wholly on their own. There would be no supplies, no directions, no help in case of trouble. They would live off the country or die.

Living off the country had been easy, so far. Small game was plentiful. They could generally shoot elk or antelope for fresh meat. The larger watercourses abounded in fish. For a special treat, the hunters often trailed down the prairie bees and came back with the prize of spicy sage honey and a number of stings for mementos. Now and again they had met with Indians who were very ready to trade dried pumpkin, maize and beans for cloth or beads.

The members were now trail-hardened. But the fat living had inclined the less experienced to take a light view of the necessary discipline. So far, it had been a picnic, with one or two disagreeable episodes. They took the cheerful and foolish view that everything would continue to be fine. Why worry? And why sweat themselves thin with useless routine?

The vivid example made of sleepy Slim from Ohio had faded from their minds. They grumbled and they shirked, although there was no open mutiny. But the expedition was not being run to the satisfaction of the leaders. Walker, Young, and Gregg spoke to Captain Becknell in the evening camp outside Council Grove. The four men decided to call a meeting after supper.

As the meeting opened, the leader sat on the high seat of his Pittsburgh wagon, puffing at a blackened pipe. He removed it from his lips and spoke.

"You fellows have had a pretty soft time of it so far."

Several voices were raised in contradiction. It was not their notion of soft living at all.

"It'll be harder from now on," Becknell told them.

"Why should it be?" somebody asked challengingly.

"Nobody knows what's out there." The leader pointed toward the setting sun. "We have to be ready for anything."

The general feeling was expressed by a tough young teamster who said scornfully, "Who's afraid!" Set him up with a good smoothbore rifle, a handful of powder, and a bullet between his teeth, and he'd stand off any ten Pawnees or Shawnees or Comanches. "Who's afraid!" he repeated.

"I am," Captain Becknell said quietly.

"And, if the Cap's afraid, there's plenty to be afraid of," the *madre* said.

"You've traveled this way before, ain't you?" a trapper asked of Becknell.

"Yes. Once each way."

"And you came through with a whole skin."

"And lucky to do it," was Becknell's grim reply.

"If it was safe then, why ain't it safe now?" the man persisted. "Why can't we just follow your trail?"

"Because I didn't leave any," the leader said. "Nobody has, so far. Maybe this *atajo* will be the first. Well, boys," he continued briskly. "Final stock-up tomorrow at the trading post. Inspection at sundown. We hit the trail at sunrise. Santa Fe or bust! Goodnight."

The store did a rush of trade the next day. For the journey each man must have fifty pounds of flour, fifty of bacon, ten of coffee, and a sufficient supply of sugar and salt. A large tin cup and his skinning knife made up his table utensils. He carried a gun; usually a long barreled rifle, though a few preferred "scatterguns," as shotguns were called. To serve the weapon, the hunter had one hundred flints, twenty-five pounds of black powder, one hundred pounds of lead, and a bullet mold to cast the lead into bullets.

To prepare his weapon for action, the gunner rammed the powder down the barrel, and followed it with the bullet wadded in cloth or coarse paper. He sprinkled a few grains of powder on the firing pan, set his flint above the pan, cocked the hammer of his gun and let go. The hammer hit the flint and struck out sparks. The sparks set fire to the powder flecks in the pan. The fire was communicated to the charge in the barrel. With a mighty bang and a fearful kick, the bullet sped on its deadly errand. At least, that was the theory.

The fact was often different. Half the time, the charge failed to explode at the first impact of the hammer. Then, if the object at the other end of the barrel was a bear or an Indian, the man with the gun had better drop it and take to his heels.

Trappers carried half-a-dozen steel beaver traps with chains, weighing six pounds each. Every member of an expedition had, swinging at his belt, the large "possible sack." This was filled with everything possible to cram into it: thread, buttons, oil, needles, leather and cloth patches, tobacco, small tools, and even—for the delicate—tooth brushes and combs.

The trader at Council Grove charged very high prices for all these items. The men paid. They had to have them to pass Captain Becknell's final inspection. At the close of the day's business the storekeeper took Gregg and Ewing Young aside.

"Got the newest thing in trade here," he said, with a wink.

"No go," Gregg replied. "The Captain don't believe in the whiskey trade with Indians."

"Neither do I," the trader said. "It drives 'em crazy and they go on the warpath and then there's killings. This isn't firewater. It's music." He brought out a box full of jewsharps.

Young stared. "I've met a heap of Indians," he said. "But I never yet saw one that was musical."

"So they ain't," the trader agreed. "But they're crazy after this contraption. It tickles their teeth. Dollar apiece."

The two men cautiously invested five dollars each. Later they regretted their caution when they sold their first tooth-tickler to a Sawkey chief for the equivalent of five dollars. The last one, several weeks later, went to a Comanche warrior for a three-ounce white-gold nugget worth fifty dollars.

12

A Grim Lesson

TRAVEL FROM STREAM BOTTOM TO STREAM
bottom was easy and pleasant. From the depths
of his possible sack, Ewing Young brought up
fishhooks and line. The fish were willing. One
day a twenty-five-pound blue catfish was caught.
The travelers picked its bones.

Daily the hunters brought in prairie chicken, wild turkey, and quail. The men ate everything and called for more. Pete, the *madre*, wore himself thin over his spits and kettles. He declared that it was the "most bulimious outfit ever a man cooked for." "Bulimy" was trail-speech for a big appetite.

The softer the caravan lived, the laxer it became. Several of the volunteer watchers went back on their offer to stand guard each night. This threw more work on the faithful. The little band of Becknell supporters grew thin and nerve-wracked with weariness. It was only a question of time as to when the strain would be too much for their iron endurance.

After a few days' journey, the river narrowed. A wagon which attempted the passage around the shoulder of a cliff became mired in quicksand and was hauled back with difficulty. The trailmaster ordered the caravan to cut across prairie.

Hardly had the outriders spread out when one came hurrying back with a report of a large band of Indians in war formation to the northwest. The band came nearer. Trapper Jim, whose eyesight was the sharpest in the outfit, watched the approaching band between his cupped hands and then burst into hoarse laughter. The "Indians," he reported, were wearing horns. In fact, they were a herd of elk. The men spent a lively day hunting them and killed two.

This further convinced the anti-Becknell party that there was nothing to be feared in a country where Indians turned out to be elk.

Two days later, the youthful Ohioan came to Captain Becknell.

"Captain, I been out on sentry six nights running."

"So have the rest of us, young fellow," the captain replied.

"Last night I went to sleep standing up, and fell over."

"Tell the *madre* to give you an extra pail of strong coffee."

"I'm scairt I can't keep awake even with that," the boy insisted.

"All right," the leader said patiently. "I'll divide up your watch tonight with Young."

The exhausted youth refused that. But he was

nearly at the end of his rope. The other watchers were in no better shape. The relief came none too soon.

It was on a hot June afternoon when they sighted a dark hump ahead of them. It proved to be a dead buffalo bull. The hunters reported that he was very old, and had probably been abandoned by the herd to die of old age.

Ewing Young was not satisfied. Anything might have important meaning on the trail. He made a careful investigation and came back with a sober face to speak privately with Captain Becknell.

"That buffalo's got a bullet hole in his neck and a broken arrow between his ribs," said Young.

The leader rubbed his head. "That's bad," he said. "Redskins and white men hunting the same range."

The trailmaster nodded. "Yes, that might mean trouble."

"What was the arrow?" Becknell asked.

"Looked like an Arapaho," Young replied.

"How long has the bull been dead?"

"Not more than a day," Young answered.

Becknell reflected. "We'll close up the formation," he decided. "But say nothing to the men."

That evening's camp was pitched near a small grove of aspens. At sundown the wind shifted. Trapper Jim, who had been rubbing oil into his high boots to keep them soft and comfortable, lifted his head. His nose wriggled sensitively. He went over to speak a word in Captain Becknell's ear. The leader got his long rifle and looked to the priming. Trapper Jim returned to the wagon to get his weapon and load it. He wet his forefinger with his lips and held it up to the wind. The two men left camp, making a wide swing to the left.

They approached the small woodland cautiously and edged in among the trees. Soon they were in sight of the abandoned Indian camp.

It was a small one, as was shown by the size of the fire, now dead. Beside it was an object which had once been human. It was a bearded head impaled on a stake. The beard proved that the victim was a white man. The scalp had been cut away. Several arrows were still in the neck. Silently the two completed their investigation and turned away.

Back in camp Captain Becknell's voice roused those who had already gone to sleep and startled the others by its tone.

"I want every man who voted against standing guard to follow me."

They gathered and straggled out. This time the leader took a straight line. He beckoned his followers into the dusk of the woodpatch. When they were all there, he lifted the stake with the head atop it.

"Take a look," he said grimly, "and see what nice, safe country we're in."

He led the way back. Nobody spoke until they reached the wagons. Then the leader lifted his voice again.

"You've seen what you've seen. What do you think of it?"

Silence.

"Don't like it, eh?" Becknell went on. "You thought you knew more than I do about the trail. What do you think now?"

An uneasy shuffling of feet was the only answer.

"All right," said Captain Becknell. "Now listen to me. Anybody that doesn't like the way this *atajo* is run, can quit and be his own *atajo*. But from now on this camp is going to be run by rule-and-rote. You'll take orders from the trail captain by day and the camp captain by night. You'll form the wagons. You'll hobble the critters. You'll take 'em out to feed and fetch 'em in to march. You'll stand sentry-go. You'll dig trenches when it rains, and you'll douse fires when it's clear."

The Captain looked from one shamed face to another. "Hard work?" he went on. "Certes, it's hard work. What did you expect when you signed up? Lace napkins with your grub? This *atajo* is no place for pinky-fingers and lilylivers. That's all. Any remarks?"

There were none. From that time on the camp ran like clockwork.

13

"Para *Swap*"

THIS TIME IT WAS NOBODY'S FAULT. EVEN HARD-
bitten Captain Becknell had to admit that. Four of
his best men were on outpost—Trapper Jim, William Wolfskill, Pete the *madre*, and Ohio Slim,
who had learned his lesson.

"And cheap at three dollars," Slim admitted every time he remembered the lesson.

They had warning, too. That noon, when they had stopped near a dry stream bed for their two-hour rest, the leader had given special instructions to the cook. No hardwood was to be used for the dinner fire; nothing but dry aspen. Aspen burns clear and gives off no smoke. Across that gently rolling prairie, smoke would be visible for a long distance.

"Injuns, boss?" Pete asked his leader.

"Might be," was Becknell's cautious answer.

"You ain't seen any?"

"No."

"But you think there's some around?" Pete insisted.

"Might be," Captain Becknell repeated.

"It's my opinion," Pete confided to Trapper Jim, "that the boss can smell an Injun ten miles down wind."

The alarm came in the first watch. Camp had been pitched in the open prairie. At this spot the soil was poor and the grass short and dry. The animals spread far afield to get enough to eat.

A dull thunder broke the silence of the night. Wolfskill, on sentry, caught it first.

"Buffalo!" he shouted. "Bearing this way."

Buffalo herds do not stampede at night unless driven by some alarm. The watchful Joe Walker yelled a warning.

"Indians! Rifles out."

The aroused campers tumbled out, fumbling for their weapons. But the charging herd at the last moment swerved away from the camp in a long sweep. This trick was known to Captain Becknell.

"The Indians are running off our stock," he shouted.

The scared horses and mules were caught up in the stampede and scattered. Some, in their terror, burst their hobbles. Evidence was found afterward that other hobbles had been cleanly cut.

The whole camp turned out in pursuit, leaving the wagons unguarded. This was what the Indians had hoped and planned. They were not after the horses. They wanted loot. There was plenty of it in the wagons. When the exhausted campers returned at dawn, with three horses and two mules still missing, they had another and more dismal surprise.

Their belongings were strewn about the ground. The packs had been hastily rifled. Worst of all, their spare weapons were gone. Nobody had so much as seen an Indian.

Captain Becknell shook his fists at the sky and cursed himself for a fool. Tricked like a greenhorn by a bunch of thieving Osages!

"How do you know they're Osages?" Wolfskill asked curiously.

"Pawnees or Comanches would have attacked," the leader said. "Osages don't fight; they steal."

Young Ohio Slim bristled up. "Aren't we going after 'em?"

"Where?" said Captain Becknell heavily.

Where, indeed? The raiders had left neither trace nor trail.

As the camp was breaking later in the morning, a horseman appeared making elaborate peace signs. Chateau, the chieftain of a band camped a few miles away, wished to pow-wow with the white captain. Would the white Captain come to the Chief's camp?

The white Captain would not. If the Indian Chief wanted to pow-wow, they would meet in the open.

It was so arranged. Chateau explained politely that it was all a mistake. His warriors did have some of the white man's guns, but arrangements could be made for their return.

"Warriors!" the Captain said. "Thieves!"

"*Para* swap," the Osage blandly suggested in a mixture of Spanish and Yankee.

"*Para* swap!" repeated the angry leader. "You steal our guns and then you want us to swap for 'em. What'll you take?"

It appeared that the looters had been scared off before they had obtained all that they had hoped for. Their squaws needed beads. The warriors would be glad to have some mirrors and some of the funny things that gave thrills to teeth. *Para* swap?

There was nothing else for it. The caravan had to have its arms back. The deal went through. A jubilant band of Osages took jaunty leave of an unhappy bunch of whites.

14

The Trail Forks

HALF WAY!

The train of men, mules, and horses halted on a high bank overlooking the Great Bend of the Arkansas. Far below them ran the stream, broad and bright and swift. It was the biggest water they had seen since leaving Missouri six weeks before.

Groves of tall trees gave a welcome shade. There was rich grass for the stock. Looking down on the plain, they could see deer and antelope. It was a pleasant country.

Thanks to the careful leadership of Captain Becknell, the caravan was in good condition. A loss of ten or fifteen animals would not have been unusual. They had lost but five: the horse that had been buried in the landslide, another which had been swept away in a freshet, and three mules. One of these had been bitten by a rattlesnake and disabled. Another had been run down and eaten by wolves. The third had broken its hobbles and trotted away at night to join a herd of buffalo, where it may have been welcome. Anyway, it never came back.

There had been some delays caused by breakage on the wagons. That was to be expected. But there were skilled repairmen in the outfit. No wagon had to be abandoned.

The men were hardy and in good spirits.

When the trailmaster announced that the journey was half over and they would take a day's lay-off, there was much good cheer. Two members went out with scatterguns and brought in a generous supply of game birds. Anglers had no difficulty in catching a variety of fish.

Pete aroused high enthusiasm when he trailed a hungry bear to a berry patch. After he chased the animal away (he didn't *think* it was a grizzly, he said, but it might have been) he gathered enough berries for a fresh fruit pie all around. There were men in the *atajo* who hadn't seen pie in a year.

Boats would have been useful now. But it would take too long to build craft large enough to float the wagons and the stock. Rafts could be thrown together quickly. But the two rivermen, after studying the current, discouraged Captain Becknell from trying to raft against it. It was too swift.

The expedition skirted the north bank for five days. At noon of the sixth they came upon a reach where the water rippled over bright, pebbly shallows. The leader got out his home-drawn map and examined it.

"They say there's only two safe fords on this whole river," he said to his companions, who crowded around to look at the map.

"This looks like it might be one of 'em," Gregg remarked.

"Reckon it is," Becknell said.

"What do we want of a ford?" Trapper Jim asked wonderingly.

Instead of answering directly, the leader began to talk about the country like a schoolmarm to her class. The *atajo*, he said, had now reached the fork of the route. The straightest line to Santa Fe led across the ford into little-known badlands. Somewhere beyond the waterless plains there was a river which the Indians called the Bull, and the Mexicans, the Cimarron. It was known mainly by hearsay. No two reports about it were alike. From what could be pieced together, it appeared that the water in the river had strange habits. In some places the current ran above ground; in others, underground. It varied from season to season.

As to the country the travelers would have to cross before reaching this strange river, there was no such uncertainty. All accounts described it as

difficult and dangerous. The entire distance between the Arkansas and the Cimarron was waterless and almost lifeless.

But how great was the distance? There was no
certain information on that vital point. Indians
had successfully made the passage. So much was
known. Where an Indian could go, a white man
could follow. That was Captain Becknell's belief,
particularly if the white man was named Becknell,

"So there it is," he said, folding the map.
"Who's for the south with me?"

"And leave the river?" a voice asked dubiously.

"There's other rivers besides this one," the
Captain said.

"The good old wet Arkansas is good enough
for me," a grizzled mountain man asserted.

"I don't like the looks of that country," a
wagoner put in, peering out across the flat and
lifeless expanse.

"I don't even like the smell of it," added a
mule-man, sniffing at a hot blast of air from that
quarter.

"Ain't that Mexico on the other side?" another
member asked.

"The maps ain't what you might call particular as to that," the Captain admitted. "Some folks say one thing, some say another."

"What do the Mexicans say?" a mule-man inquired.

"I reckon they claim it."

"They can have it for all of me," Pete put in. "The Mexicans have a saying about that country. They say that a bachelor wolf with no family dependent on him couldn't make his living there."

"You know what they call that stretch, boss?" Joe Walker said, and answered his own question. "Jornada del Muerto."

"Journey of Death," Becknell confirmed gravely. "But it's the shortest trail and the flattest. Easy on the wagons."

Faro Mike took this up. "Trail? Who made it?"

"Nobody yet," the Captain said. "We'll make our own."

"Yeh, but where to?" a teamster asked.

"The Cimarron River. The rest'll be easy."

One of the fur-trappers said uneasily, "I've heard it was a thirsty country."

Walker said, "One rain a year is figured to be a wet season."

Ewing Young turned to him. "You've been across on the other side, haven't you, Joe?"

The campmaster nodded. "A couple of years ago."

"What did you find?"

"Not the Cimarron," said Ewing Young. "But it wasn't for want of looking. I was glad to get back to Arkansas water. It's a tough piece of map."

Captain Becknell looked soberly about the circle. "I don't claim that the trip will be an Independence Day picnic with a liberty pole and free victuals and the Silver Cornet Band playing Yankee Doodle," he said. "I only say it's the direct route and I'm taking it."

"Is it an order, Cap?" the gambler asked respectfully enough.

"No sir!" was the emphatic reply. "This isn't even a vote. Every man to decide for himself and no hard feelings."

Free discussion followed. One member said he had heard unpleasant things about the desert Indians. He liked his scalp where it was and preferred to keep it there. Another said that he wasn't afraid of the redskins, but when he wanted a drink of water, he wanted it; he'd stick to the good old Arkansas. A third pointed out that there was no hurry. Why take such a risk when there was plenty of time? Then a young muleteer spoke up.

"I bet I know what the Captain's after. That gold and jewels and stuff in the Lost Cities. You on that Cibola trail, Cap? If you are, I'm with you."

The leader grinned. "Well, I reckon Cibola is just as likely to be out there as anywhere."

Harmon Gregg looked hard at his chief. "You're sure you're set on going, Bill?"

"Sure as I am that Job had boils," Becknell said.

"All right. I'm with you."

"Count me in," Walker said.

"And me." "And me." "And me." The responses came from Young, Trapper Jim, and the Ohioan. William Wolfskill said he had never seen a real desert and he reckoned this was his chance. Three of the muleteers followed.

That would be enough for two wagons. Beck-nell was satisfied. Ewing Young said:

"We'll sweat a heap out there. What about waterscrape?" This was the frontier term for water supply carried by the pack animals or in the wagons.

"We've got plenty of *ollas*," the leader replied, pointing to a row of small earthenware jars.

Young looked them over doubtfully. "Say, Cap, how far you reckon this Cimarron water is?"

"Forty miles. Maybe forty-five."

"I'd figure on sixty," Walker advised.

"We'll travel by night and lay up by day," the leader said. "That'll be easier on the livestock. We ought to make twenty miles between sundown and sunup. There's plenty of water in the Cimarron when we get there, I reckon."

"God help us if there isn't," Harmon Gregg said soberly.

They did not get there.

15

Thirst

A JACK-RABBIT REARED UP ON HIS FURRY
haunches and stared across the flat and lifeless
plain. He was surprised. He had lived in that
country a long time, but he had never seen anything like the cavalcade winding in and out
among the spiky greasewood bushes. These crea-

tures were not buffalo and they were not antelope, and they certainly were not bear or deer. It was Jack's first sight of human beings and their mode of travel. Hence he had no way of knowing that this strange sight was a wagon train.

These odd creatures might be unfriendly to jack-rabbits, he decided. He lowered himself cautiously to his forepaws and went about his business in a series of long bounds which could outdistance anything slower than an arrow.

The rabbit's fears were well founded. The men in and around those two wagons would gladly have killed him. They would have killed any living creature with blood in its veins. For this was Captain Becknell's group in search of the Cimarron River. They had been out for two nights and three days, and they were hopelessly lost. Their last drop of water had been finished that noon. Baked out by the withering heat, they had killed their two dogs and divided the blood. It kept them alive but did little to quench their thirst.

How had they lost their way? Nobody could tell. Their compass was a poor thing. But there

were the stars to steer by at night, and the cruel
sun by day. Something had gone wrong in their
reckoning. They had come upon the banks of
what once was a creek. The bottom was dry sand.
It may have been Sand River. It was not the
sought-for Cimarron. Becknell cut branches from
the bushes and set them up. In the midst of his
bitter suffering, he still wanted to leave landmarks
for others who might possibly come that way.

At the close of the third day, he gathered the
handful of his followers.

"We've got just one chance," he told them.

They waited silently.

"To get back to the Arkansas."

"How far?" Walker croaked from a dried-out
throat.

"I don't just exactly know," the leader admitted.

"Which direction?" William Wolfskill asked.

"North. We're sure of that much, anyway."

Ewing Young, who carried the uncertain compass, snatched it from his pocket, flung it down
on the sand, and kicked it. It was a childish gesture.
Men fevered from want of water are likely to act

abnormally. Captain Becknell looked at his old friend with a kindly grin.

"Give it another kick for me, Ewing," he said. "I'll take my bearings by the North Star."

Trapper Jim thrust his finger down his throat to press the swollen tongue into place. "What are the chances of our making it, Cap?" he wheezed.

"We've got to make it," the leader said firmly. "When there's only one chance you've got to take it."

"We can kill the mules," someone muttered.

"And go on foot? Might as well cut our own throats," Gregg said.

"I'll shoot the man that lays a hand on a mule of mine," Trapper Jim said savagely.

"How long can the critters last?" Walker asked.

The men looked at one another haggardly. Twenty-four hours earlier a quart of water, sorely needed by the men, had been given to each animal. They could still plod. But two of them looked sick.

Captain Becknell gave the orders. They were

to spread out, on the chance of finding a *tenaja* (a natural tank) of rainwater. It was a chance in a thousand, but they must take every chance. If water was found, the signal would be three gunshots. In that lifeless stillness, a shot could be heard for many miles. Every man was to head due north. When he could walk no longer, he was to crawl into the wagon, and his place would be taken by another.

It was a night of torture. The next day was worse. The agonized men saw shimmering lakes of blue before them, which vanished as they advanced. This was not delirium. It was the cruel mirage of the desert.

Young Ohio Slim came staggering back to the wagon at noon, babbling that he had seen one of the Lost Cities, glittering with gold and silver. And here were the jewels they had heard of! He emptied his pockets of the sand he had scrabbled up. The sun, pouring its rays down from above, had addled his brain.

The men knew that they could not last through another day, probably not through that night.

Their tongues were turning black, a sign that death was but a few hours away. They slit the ears of the patient mules to get a little blood.

At sunset Trapper Jim dropped. He lay in the sand, waiting to die.

The strong-willed Becknell unhitched the freshest mule from the wagon, mounted it, and rode on. He had no hope, no expectation of finding anything. But it was not in him to give up. The spirit of the pioneer drove him on.

A dark form appeared on the skyline, moving in his direction. Becknell wheeled his mule and dug his spurless heels into its flanks. Throwing himself from its back, he seized his gun and loaded it. Then he loaded Trapper Jim's weapon. Two shots were better than one. But could he rouse his companion? Was the trapper still alive?

He pushed the sprawled body to a sitting posture and shook it violently. Through his parched lips he forced one word in a dry croak.

"Buffalo."

Trapper Jim staggered to his feet. A buffalo! If they could kill it, that might mean life for them. He brought his rifle to his shoulder. He could not speak; his tongue was too swollen. But he rammed an extra-heavy charge of powder down the smooth barrel.

The great animal came lumbering on. It was an old bull, weak and half blind. Its belly sagged. Scenting the mules, it stopped. Becknell fired. A red weal streaked the bull's shoulder too high to do much harm. He swerved and increased his pace.

"Shoot! Shoot!" the Captain shouted to Trapper Jim.

Jim sighted carefully and pulled the trigger. But his eyes were swollen and blurred with suffering. As he heard the explosion, he knew that his aim had not been true. The recoil of the overcharge knocked him sprawling. When he turned over and pushed himself up on his hands for a look, he saw that he had not wholly missed. The buffalo was limping on his right fore-quarter, but was still pluckily lumbering on. He topped the rise and was lost to view.

For the first time Captain Becknell's courage broke under the strain of disappointment. He threw himself flat in the sand and lay. Trapper

Jim raised a distorted face to the pitiless glare of the sky. Their last chance, they thought, was gone.

A shot sounded nearby, just across the rise, followed by a hoarse, exultant yell.

"Got him!"

The two unsuccessful marksmen staggered in the direction of the voice. A hundred yards in front of them, the buffalo had slumped in a massive heap of fur. William Wolfskill was running toward the spot. They joined him with knives drawn. His bullet had split the animal's heart.

"I heard your shots and got here just in time," he panted.

They were in luck. The swollen belly of the bull was heavy with undigested water, gallons of it. They drank and drank till they could swallow no more, then took a pailful of the filthy and precious liquid to the wagon where Gregg lay, semi-conscious. He revived at once. They held a hasty council over the dead body of the buffalo bull.

Wherever the bull had found the water, it could not be far off. Could they pick up his trail and follow it? Darkness was coming on. They set themselves to study the ground. The hoofprints led them to the northeast. From a ridge they made out a clump of trees, taller than any desert growth. The search was over. Not waiting to reach the waterhole which they knew to be there, they fired the triple signal.

No answer was heard. By this they knew that their companions were either too far distant to hear or too far gone to answer. After refreshing themselves and their animals, they filled up the containers with the clear water and scattered. One wagon they found still doggedly headed north, the men only half conscious. They were revived and helped to track down the remaining mule riders. There was a joyous gathering that night at the waterhole. The animals were no less thankful than the men.

An easy morning jog brought them back to the Arkansas. All were well content to follow it and the old route except Captain Becknell. He had left his marks behind him. He still believed in the short Cimarron route.

Some day it would be found.

16

A Wilderness Haven

MEN DYING OF HUNGER REQUIRE LONG DAYS TO
restore their strength. Men who are near death
from thirst return to health more quickly. Captain
Becknell's group were of tough fiber. They decided that two days' rest would be enough. For
that brief spell they took life easy at the ford.

They lolled in the cooling waters of the Arkansas. Their weary animals got a needed rest.

The third morning dawned with a dash of rain. The leader pointed out an undeniable fact:

"This isn't getting us any nearer Santa Fe."

"Let's get going," Gregg agreed, and other voices expressed readiness.

The reduced *atajo* took up again the brisk routine of the start.

"Ready?" from the trailmaster.

"All ready."

"Catch up!"

The word spurred them to the familiar contest as to who should be first. Soon the triumphant call of the spryest sounded:

"All set!"

"Fall in." The line formed. Then, "Stretch out," and once more they were on the move westward.

Captain Becknell had studied his map by the light of a buffalo-tallow "dip" candle the night before. He had no great faith in its accuracy. Unless it was wholly untrustworthy, however, somewhere upstream from them was Chouteau's island.

It might be inhabited or it might be abandoned; he had no means of knowing. He was by no means certain that he could even identify the place. Whatever buildings had once been there might well have been swallowed up by the forest growth. He said nothing about it to his men.

They now traveled with an advantage which they had not enjoyed before. They had a plain trail to follow, the track of the wagon wheels of those who had chosen the easier route. They had no need to scout ahead in order to avoid obstacles in their path. The men who had gone over the trail before had done that for them.

The course was an easy, steady climb toward the distant mountains, through grassy uplands with frequent patches of woods. Tributary streams, some dry, cut across the road here and there and slowed down the progress of the *atajo*. Often the banks of these streams were steep with sides of loose soil. In the worst places the men had to unload their wagons at the bottom, and haul them up the banks of the streams with ropes. The mules were then called upon to pack the merchandise to the summit for re-loading. This was not always enough. The humans often helped out as beasts of burden, toiling up and down the dangerous and crumbling cliffside with overloaded packs.

At Little Rabbit Creek, Trapper Jim's wagon broke a rear axle. The whole outfit was held up for a day while he searched for, found, and trimmed a hardwood bough suitable as a substitute. Farther along a horse got into a patch of loco weed and filled up on the "crazy plant" before he was discovered. His antics stampeded the other animals. Four hours were wasted in rounding them up.

Delays annoyed Captain Becknell. He kept hoping to catch up with the group of men who had kept to the Arkansas and refused to look for the Cimarron. At one time, he judged by the marks, this group was hardly twenty-four hours in advance of them.

Then, without apparent reason, the trail disappeared at a low spot where a stretch of gravel interrupted the broad green level of the prairie. Not even Trapper Jim's keen eyes could find wheel marks.

"That's all right," Harmon Gregg pointed out. "Last night's rain washed 'em out."

"Then we'll pick 'em up in the grass opposite," the trapper said.

They fanned out across the space looking for the break in the tall growth. There was no sign of it. The thing was unbelievable. Wagon trains do not vanish into thin air, leaving no trace. To be sure, the caravan ahead might have turned into the river. But why? At the Big Bend, where the two groups parted company, the others had shown a marked distaste for the southern bank and its arid desert. What could have happened to change their minds?

Captain Becknell climbed a near-by rise for a better view. He pointed toward something which a patch of trees had shut off from sight below.

"Auguste Chouteau's island," he shouted.

He had sighted the line of the rough log breastworks put up by Chouteau's men in 1810, when they had given the attacking Pawnees their first taste of rifle fire and successfully fought them off in an all-day battle against heavy odds. There was the fort and, what is more, some of the logs looked quite new. That would be evidence that the island was then or recently had been occupied. He cupped his hands and called.

Figures ran out from the shelter of the trees and waved them to come over. They were Becknell's own men. The Captain rode his mule across and demanded an explanation.

Faro Mike gave it, not without embarrassment. After the party split, he had been chosen leader. They got along all right for two weeks or so. Then the men became careless. One night in the dark of the moon, a small band of Indians had crept past a sleeping sentry, stampeded the imperfectly hobbled livestock, and run off twelve head. Mike was through. He wanted nothing better than to hand back the command to Becknell.

The others backed him to a man. Under Becknell's resumed command the band was a solid unit again.

As they prepared to leave, the representative of the Chouteau interests gave Captain Becknell some parting advice. A band of Pawnees was somewhere nearby. They might want to trade. Or they might want to raid.

"You never can tell about Pawnees," he said.

At any rate, the caravan would be wise to stick together and make the best speed they could. Stragglers would be in danger. The best plan would be to stay close to the Arkansas.

"We won't get much fur that way," the Captain said. "What about the back country?"

The other was not communicative. He had been kindly and hospitable to the wayfarers under his roof, as was the rule of the wilderness. But it was plain that he did not want them hunting or trapping around there.

One of the island men chuckled and said, "Demandez à Mcnsieur 'Atch." (Ask Mr. Hatch.)

"Who's Hatch?" Becknell asked curiously.

"Some folks don't believe there's any such person," the head man answered. That was all he would say on the subject. Wolfskill, who understood French, overheard the man who had first spoken remark that there were some things it wasn't lucky to talk about.

Farewells were exchanged. The *atajo* forded the river again and turned their faces westward.

17

Santa Fe at Last

THE MEN OF THE EXPEDITION RETURNED TO THE
route in fine condition. From a business viewpoint
they were not doing so well. Some of their goods
had been wasted through carelessness in the early
days before they had come under the discipline of

the trail. One whole pack was lost with the horse which was swept away in the Little Arkansas.

Other merchandise had gone in the "swaps" with the thievish Osages. The stock must be replaced. It would not do to go into Santa Fe short of trade goods.

The answer was to get fur. This was always marketable.

But where were the fur animals? Certainly not along the Arkansas River bottom. Chouteau's men had cleaned out that once rich trapping-ground.

The mountain men were for scattering in small groups through the back country. Captain Becknell said no to that plan. With warlike savages ranging the region, the party must hang together for protection. He was willing to give them a reasonable time to trap, but the safety of the party must be considered before anything else.

Every night around the campfires, the members talked about fur. They were in high country now and still climbing. The hides ought to be in first-rate condition if they could find them. But where were they to look?

They were about to break camp one morning

in a high mountain meadow overlooking the river when a distant shot startled them. It rolled and echoed and reverberated from cliff to cliff.

Instantly the system of defence which Captain Becknell had perfected went into motion. The grazing animals were herded swiftly within the hollow square of the wagons. Under the wagons the men were coolly loading and priming their long rifles, each holding a spare bullet between his teeth.

"Listen for the whistle," somebody called.

The Pawnees, while they hunted or made war, were in the habit of using signal whistles of willow or, if they could get them in trade, of metal.

Silence followed the shot.

William Wolfskill walked over to where Captain Becknell was talking to his lieutenants. "That was no Indian," he said.

"How do you know?" Ewing Young asked sharply.

"It was a full charge of powder."

"That's right," Joseph Walker confirmed. "You can tell by the report."

"What if it was a full charge?" the Captain

asked. The Kentuckian had gained a reputation for knowing about firearms.

"Back where I come from," Wolfskill explained, "no Indian uses more than half a charge. They hoard their powder. I reckon they're all alike in that."

"I guess that's right, too," Becknell agreed. "We'll wait and take a look."

They advanced to the brow of the cliff and got down behind a fringe of chaparral. Presently there appeared at the upper end of the defile two mules and a man. All of them were shaggy, grimy, and trail-worn. One mule carried a thin pack. The other carried the man and a fresh-killed, white-tailed fawn.

Captain Becknell stood up. "Howdy!" he hailed them.

The two mules pulled up and waggled their ears in surprise. The rider's hand twitched on his rifle but was at once raised in salute.

"Howdy," he responded.

"Where's your outfit?" the Captain asked.

The stranger pointed at the two mules. "Right here," he answered.

The other Becknell men had now risen beside their leader. "Is that all there is of you?" Harmon Gregg asked suspiciously.

"That's all," the other answered gravely.

The men of the *atajo* stared at one another. They had all heard tales of lone rangers who lived and throve in the unknown back country, but they took little stock in such stories.

Captain Becknell had a thought. "You wouldn't be Hatch, would you?"

The stranger looked pleased. "That's me," he said. "Hatch."

A voice back of the scrub shouted, "Grub in five minutes."

"Come and join us," Captain Becknell invited cordially.

"I'll do that and thank ye," Hatch answered.

There was some delay before he appeared. When he walked into the breakfast circle he had changed his costume. He now had on a buckskin coat as stiff as a board fence. It went on over his head like a barrel. He never sat down in the open, or went to sleep, he explained, without putting it on. Soaked thoroughly in water and sun-hardened, the hide would turn the point of a war arrow.

"There's Indians around, then," the trailmaster said quickly.

"Not now," Hatch answered.

"Baptiste back at Chouteau's island warned us about a band of Pawnees."

A small smile appeared in the depths of Hatch's whiskers. "That's to scare you off," he said.

"Why would he want to scare us?" asked Ewing Young.

"The fewer trappers, the more game," Hatch told them.

Over *Madre* Pete's piping-hot meal, they questioned him about the prospects of trapping. Unlike the island dwellers, he freely gave his information, such as it was.

Anywhere along the small streams over the ranges, he told them, there was plenty of fur. Beaver? Why, those mountain beavers grew half as big as a sheep. Otter? He'd seen otter that could lick a mountain-cat in a stand-up fight. Foxes and muskrat and suchlike, they were so thick you could catch 'em under your hat like butterflies.

"I wonder if he knows what he's talking about," Trapper Jim said a little too loudly. The guest overheard it.

"I'd ought to," he said mildly. "I been here and hereabouts going onto five year."

"Alone?" Gregg exclaimed. "And you kept your scalp?"

"Oh, Indians ain't so bad if you know how to meet 'em," Hatch said with his quiet smile.

"How do you go about it if you meet up with a band?" Walker asked curiously.

"I say 'Howdy? Trade?' And we trade."

"Just as simple as that!" Ewing Young commented. He had the answer—or thought he had. "Indians won't harm a crazy man," he explained to his companions. "They most likely think he's exalted in the head—crazy."

"Maybe I am," said Hatch. "But I get along."

Borrowing a pencil and a bit of paper, he drew them an offhand map of the country and bade them good-bye. They never saw him again.

"There," Pete said as he disappeared down the slope, "goes the prize liar since Ananias."

That was the general opinion. But there was the map. It was worth trying. They scattered to investigate the indicated streams without too much faith in the result.

They were never more mistaken in their lives. The talkative Mr. Hatch might have exaggerated a little but he knew his business. Setting and re-setting the traps kept the whole company busy. Jim and the mountain man with whom he was teaming took thirty beaver from one pool. The largest of the catch shaded one hundred pounds. Several went over sixty.

The *atajo* spent ten days along the streams, and took out more than three thousand dollars' worth of furs. These were scraped, cured, and packaged. The valuable pelt, beaver or otter, was carefully folded, the hairy side within. When enough layers had been set, green buckskin thongs were tied around the bundle. Drying out, these bands tight-ened with the power of a vise. The pelts were compressed to iron hardness without damage to the fur. A standard pack was eighty beaver or

sixty otter skins. Small-fry operators would pack as many as six hundred muskrat pelts in a single bundle.

Every wagon was overloaded as the *atajo* left the Arkansas and struck south into Mexico. Every pack animal was groaning and protesting against the extra weight on its back. All the men were happy. The going was easy now, down-slope from the mountains, through a well-watered country where the Indians were peaceful and there were many Mexican settlements.

Santa Fe was as trade-greedy as the Becknell men had heard and hoped. They made their sales, of both fur and trade-goods, almost before the merchandise could be unstrapped from the animals and unloaded from the "Pittsburghs" for display.

Hip-hip-hooray
For Santa Fe!

the caravan whooped.

When the last dollar had been counted out and the poorer animals sold for what they would bring, the men were in no haste to leave Santa Fe.

They had changed their minds about the place. Living was easy and comfortable there. The trail was tough going, at best. Why hurry home?

But the American of that period was never content to take life easy very long at a time. The pioneer blood in Captain Becknell's veins was soon stirring with the impulse to get going again. Ewing Young, Harmon Gregg, and Joseph Walker were showing the same symptoms of restlessness. The latter said to the Captain one day, as they sat over a game of dominoes in the plaza:

"When do we move? I promised to pack some snuff for those Frenchies on the island."

"What island was that, Joe?" Becknell asked innocently.

"Why, Chouteau's," the other answered in surprise.

"You going back that way?" Becknell asked.

Gregg looked up sharply. "What other way is there?" he demanded.

"I was kind of figuring on the short trail," the Captain said.

"What! The Cimarron trail?" Ewing Young

put in. "Didn't you get enough of the Jornada last time? My tongue gets thick just thinking of it."

The Captain placed his last domino, collected the stakes, and launched into argument. The other attempt on the Jornada had been a fool trick; he admitted it. A grown man ought to have more sense than to strike out across fifty miles of desert after a river like the Cimarron that might be where you thought it was and then again, more likely, might be somewhere else.

"Do you reckon you know where it is now?" Walker asked grimly.

"From this end, yes. I can go to it with my eyes shut. And when I get to it I'm going to hang to it."

"How long?" Ewing Young wanted to know.

"As long as the water holds out."

"And how will that get you across the Jornada?" Gregg challenged.

Patiently Becknell brought out a neatly inked map. *Here* was the Arkansas, plain as the nose on your face, and full of water year's end to year's end. And here or hereabouts was the Cimarron.

Between was the desert, the Jornada del Muerto, fifty miles of it or maybe sixty.

All right, then; they'd start from the Cimarron and follow it downstream until it began to sink into the desert sand. At the last good pool where the desert was narrowest, they would fill up the barrels which they would have ready in the wagons and head for the Arkansas. Three days, four days, five days; what did it matter so long as they had enough waterscrape? It was all a matter of waterscrape, taking enough with them for men and animals. They would establish a short trail that would cut off maybe a week of travel.

The Captain must have been a persuasive arguer, for the others, forgetting the peril and agony of their narrow escape, declared themselves in on his plan.

It all came out according to the Becknell program. At the last good pool they filled every receptacle, including their own stomachs, full to overflowing, and faced north. Ready? All set. Stretch out!

Early in the first afternoon Captain Becknell came upon the greasewood branches which he had cut and left as markers. He threw up his hands. In that terrible ordeal of the Jornada del Muerto, at the time when he and his companions were turning back in despair of ever finding the sought-for river, they had been within ten short miles of the Cimarron's abundant waters.

Well-stocked as they now were, they drank their fill every day. Not a mule had occasion to complain of thirst. Being in prime condition, they traveled fast. It was still high afternoon of the third day when the tall line of timber fringing the Arkansas came in sight. Out of sheer bravado Captain Becknell got out a pail, opened a fresh barrel of water, stripped to the skin, and treated himself to a refreshing shower bath on the sands of the Desert of Death.

Thus the short trail was set. It should have been safe and easy for any intelligent wayfarer. But there must have been an evil magic over the region. Travelers continued to lose their way, and several expeditions narrowly escaped death from thirst in the mirage-haunted wastes.

18

Uncle Sam Takes a Hand

CAPTAIN BECKNELL HAD SHOWN THAT IT COULD
be done. Now the United States Government undertook to make it easier. Congress authorized a
survey to be made by an expedition traveling from
the Missouri River to New Mexico. Their purpose was to lay out a trail. Waterholes were to be

shown on the map which the expedition would make as it traveled. Mounds were to be erected as landmarks.

How far this excellent idea was carried out is not known. Probably not very far. Later trailsmen paid little attention to their Uncle Sam's well-meant experiment.

At any rate, Captain Becknell did not wait for it. Early in 1824 he, Augustus Storrs, and Colonel M. M. Marmaduke formed an *atajo* on the grand scale. Becknell's two partners were merchants of standing and wealth. They enlisted seventy-eight adventurers for the journey to Santa Fe. It was to be done in style. There were twenty-five wagons, one hundred and fifty horses and mules, and thirty thousand dollars' worth of merchandise. Every member was required to have a rifle, a pistol, four pounds of powder, eight pounds of lead, and twenty days' provisions.

As compared to the twenty-five pounds of powder and one hundred pounds of lead of the former Becknell outfit, this seems a surprisingly light armament. The leaders must have expected a quick journey. But it was not so quick.

They started from Franklin on May 15 and did not reach Santa Fe until July 28. Seventy-four days for nine hundred miles' travel over a trail already established is not a good record. What delayed them? As their twenty-day supply of food was not nearly enough, they may have spent some time hunting game. Possibly they made some side trips searching for the Lost Cities of Cibola.

There is no record of trouble with Indians. Probably the redskins were awed by the size and formation of the band. By this time the Indians were familiar with the carrying quality of the long rifles and had a healthy respect for paleface marksmanship.

Santa Fe was still hungry for merchandise. And the Becknell-Storrs-Marmaduke wagons were heavy with all sorts of tempting goods. To the eager Mexicans they offered knives, buttons, ribbons, saws, files, nails, pepper, straw hats, vinegar, brooms, pails, "stationary" (as it was then spelled), neckcloths, and tar. They also had for sale a wide variety of gay-hued calicoes, merinos, and silks.

The company came back in triumph with one-hundred eighty thousand dollars in cash and ten thousand dollars' worth of furs. Six dollars return for one dollar invested was a satisfactory result!

It looked good to the enterprising merchants of St. Louis and other Far Western settlements. A western trek was started which increased steadily, year by year, until it changed the history of two nations.

Meantime, the government, as part of its trail-making scheme, undertook to make peace with the Indians. The Osages had always been reasonably friendly, though unreasonably thievish. The leaders of the two tribes, Little Osage and Great Osage, were invited to a conference at Council Grove in August, 1825. It was attended by such important figures as White Hair, Foolish Chief, Handsome Bird, Good Walker, The Owl, and Chief Without Ears. A treaty was offered to them. While they considered it, there was feasting and exchange of gifts.

A pit was dug and filled with brush which was set afire. The chiefs and the leaders of the whites formed a circle about it. Pipes were passed from mouth to mouth. Each person drew in several puffs and blew them out again in sign of friendship. The Indians then advanced one by one and spat into the fire. This was spitting out any grudge which they might have held against the palefaces.

The treaty was signed. It provided for the survey and landmarking of a road through the Osage lands with free passage for Americans and Mexicans alike. Travelers were also guaranteed camping and hunting rights and, from the tribesmen, "such friendly aid and assistance as may be in their power." It was an advantageous arrangement for the Americans. They got pretty much everything they wanted. The Osages got five hundred dollars. Since the time Manhattan Island was bought for twenty-four dollars, there had not been a more one-sided deal.

Even so, the government did not get all that it expected. The Americans thought that they were buying security with their five hundred dollars. So they were, as regards the Osages, who remained at peace with the whites. But the two tribes may have represented themselves as owning or controlling more land than was actually the case. To assure the traders safe passage, treaties with other tribes would have been advisable.

The Arapahos, the Kiotas, and the Shawnees had signed nothing. Nor had the warlike Comanches and the brave but treacherous Pawnees. They had smoked no pipe of peace. They had spat out no grudges against the encroaching whites.

Treaty or no treaty, there was trouble in store for future caravaners; plenty of it. Much of it they brought upon themselves.

19

The Opening Trail

THANKS TO THE BECKNELL EXPEDITION, ONE
danger of the trail was gone. Those who followed
need no longer fear getting lost. But there were
plenty of dangers left.

The hardy traders who set out west from the
Missouri knew that they were risking their skins

as well as their capital. Sometimes the risks were greater than the rewards.

By 1828 the main route was well traveled. But only a stone's throw from the highway the land was still wilderness. Going into the back country was a desperate venture. One hundred and twenty-six mountain men are known to have entered the wild country in 1826-27, trapping and hunting. Only sixteen are known to have come out alive.

What happened to the others? It is hardly to be supposed that all of the one hundred and ten unaccounted for were lost. Doubtless many of them drifted into less perilous ways of earning their living without reporting themselves. Doubtless, also, a great many died unrecorded and lonely deaths.

Some probably froze to death in the savage blizzards. Others, injured, disabled, or sick, may have been unable to get food and so starved. Snakes and wild animals may have accounted for others.

This region was thick with grizzly bears. There is probably no more fearless and ferocious creature in nature. A pioneer in the region reported counting two hundred and twenty of them in one day.

Grizzlies are as uncertain as they are savage. Sometimes a band of them would pay no attention to a caravan of men and animals passing by. Again, a single grizzly might take it into his head to tackle an expedition singlehanded. Then there would be time but for one shot per gun, and it had better be in a vital spot. A wounded grizzly would either kill or be killed.

Jacob Fowler, an early adventurer on the Santa Fe route, tells of one of these tragedies. The expedition of which he has left a record had stopped in a wild grape thicket above the Purgatoire River (called "Picketwire" by the mountain men) to get some of the fruit for cooking. They did not notice that a grizzly was there first. The bear seized a man named Dawson and began to claw him.

The leader of the party was Colonel Glenn, a fearless hunter. Hearing Dawson's cries, he plunged in, jammed his rifle into the animal's ribs and pulled the trigger. The gun missed fire.

At the same moment, the Colonel's dog, who

was as brave as her master, flew at the bear with such fury that it loosed its grip on its victim. The badly injured Dawson staggered away a few steps when the infuriated bear overtook him. Again Colonel Glenn's gun missed fire, and again the dog rushed in.

While the bear was chasing off the dog, both the men climbed a tree. The grizzly followed. As the Colonel frantically tried to reprime his gun, the bear dragged Dawson to the ground and fastened its powerful teeth in his skull.

Having got his flint and powder in order, Glenn fired a shot that killed the bear. It was too late for the unfortunate Dawson. He died of his injuries. Many equally tragic tales have come down from the early hunters.

But the trail-men, themselves, held the Indians responsible for most of the disappearances. Wandering bands which would not dare attack a well-armed wagon train would regard a single trapper, or a group of two or three, as their natural prey. There would be an ambush, or a sudden night attack with odds of ten or twenty to one, and nothing more would ever be heard of the trappers.

Wolves, coyotes, and buzzards would take care of what was left after the savages had finished.

This was the fate of Jedediah L. Smith, one of the first to travel those wilds in the days when every man was his own trail-maker. Nine years of experience, in which time he had probably explored more wild country than any other white man, did not teach him caution. In 1831 his caravan of twenty-three wagons and eighty-five men left the Arkansas River and struck south for the Cimarron as William Becknell had done nine years before. And, like Becknell, these more experienced travelers chose the wrong route. One might almost believe that the arid desert lay under some spell which misled the human mind.

The Smith *atajo* ran short of water. Their animals began to drop out and die. Some of the men became delirious from thirst. In the desperate hunt for water, they scattered. Stronger than his companions, the leader outdistanced them. He reached the Cimarron River alone. The only way in which he could identify it was by the sparse growth fringing the banks. Its bed was bone-dry.

He followed the course until he found a dark-hued splotch in the sand. Moisture! Throwing himself from his horse, he scooped feverishly at the sand until a little muddy water seeped in. He gulped it and waited for more. His horse followed, whinnying piteously. He needed water as much as his master.

A feathered head protruded cautiously above the river bank. Others joined it. Looking up, Smith saw the Comanches, now swelled to a band of more than twenty. He made the signs of peace and trading.

The Indians responded by flashing mirrors and waving blankets to scare his horse. As he tried to quiet the animal, a Comanche lance pierced his back. Drawing his pistol he killed two of the force and wounded another before they swarmed over him. His companions of the wagon train found his scalped remains beside a shallow basin filled with water.

Another famous leader, Miguel Robidoux of St. Louis, narrowly escaped the same fate. At the head of a fur-seeking band, he trapped the waters of the Gila River and penetrated into the country of the Papagos. With him was James Ohio Pattie, a wiser if not more experienced trail-man.

On the invitation of the Indians, Robidoux and his company of Frenchmen from St. Louis prepared to spend a night of feasting in the native village at the junction of the Salt River. Pattie took him aside.

"Do you think it's safe?" he said warningly.

"The Papagos are friendly," the Frenchman said. "Their chiefs smoked the pipe last year."

An English-speaking companion of Pattie's joined in the protest. Robidoux laughed it off. His men had been through hard days on the trail; let them have a good time for once.

"Not for us," Pattie said. "We'll camp outside."

The two found a safe place in a dry arroyo that cut back into the hills.

In the morning, Robidoux staggered into camp. He was covered with blood and delirious from thirst and fever. He told a dreadful story. At midnight, the savages had risen and slaughtered the whites. He had been clubbed in the head, but managed to get away in the darkness. So far as he knew, he was the only one to escape. This proved to be true.

"We've got to get out of here," Pattie said.

His companion agreed. "They'll be after us, certes." He jerked his head toward Robidoux. "What about him? He can't travel."

"We can't leave him," Pattie answered.

They decided to keep quiet that day, then lash the wounded man in a saddle and strike out after dark. By sunset the tough Frenchman had partly recovered. They set out.

Coming around the shoulder of a mountain, they saw three pinpoints of fire ahead.

"They've got us cut off," Pattie said.

Leaving Robidoux in charge of the horses, he and his companion, rifles in hand, went forward to reconnoiter. By the firelight they could make out a number of horses, but only two human figures. They seemed to be asleep.

It had been Pattie's idea to spy out a way to pass the band. Now he had another notion. When the sleepers got up and passed before the fire, they would offer an excellent mark. Why not shoot them and stampede the horses? This ambitious purpose the two whites discussed and agreed upon in whispers. At fifty yards range they could hardly miss. At forty or thirty-five, it would be even surer. The pair edged forward.

One of the supposed sleepers got to his feet. He addressed his companion. He spoke in English! The surprise and relief brought Pattie automatically to his feet. Instantly the two men below grabbed their guns and leveled them.

"Don't shoot!" Pattie shouted. "Friends! Friends!"

The near-by camp was roused. They were a hunting party headed by Ewing Young. There were thirty-three of them, a force sufficient to tackle the savages. They descended upon the village and burned it, after killing such warriors as were unable to get away.

As in this case, the vengeance of the whites was often in the same spirit of savagery as that of the redskins. Burning Indian villages and shooting down the fleeing squaws and papooses was not uncommon. After a victory over the Apaches, one of the expeditions killed the wounded and beheaded all the corpses. In the words of an early chronicler, they were "too much exasperated to show mercy."

Nor did the Indians enjoy a monopoly of scalping. This playful practice was common among the early trailsmen. It is doubtful even that they were imitating the savages. They may have learned the trick back East. In 1791, for instance, leading citizens of Pittsburgh combined to offer one hundred dollars in lawful currency for every Indian scalp. They insisted, however, that the scalp must have both ears attached to command the full price. What special value there is to a dead Indian's ears does not appear.

It was not always the redmen who started the trouble. Two explorers in 1828 were surprised and killed by Comanches. Their bodies were carried to the Arkansas River for burial by the caravan which found them. While the service was in progress, a small and peaceful band of Indians appeared. They were not even the same tribe as the killers of McNees and Monroe. There is no reason to suppose that they knew of the murders. Sensing the unfriendliness of the much larger force of whites, the Indians wheeled their horses and tried to escape. The whites ran them down and killed all but one, who escaped to tell the grisly tale. Is it any wonder that the Indians considered the whites as treacherous and murderous as the whites considered the Indians?

Nine-tenths of the senseless slaughter was probably avoidable. Consider the case of the Bent brothers and that great pioneer, Ceran St. Vrain. They built forts and trading posts and did business with the most ferocious of the tribes. The Arapahos, the Cheyennes, the Apaches, Comanches, and Sioux came to trust and respect them. A bargain entered into by them was faithfully carried out.

Knowing that whiskey inflamed an Indian to raiding and murder, the Bents and St. Vrain refused to carry the dangerous "firewater" in trade. At a time when savage raids and equally brutal acts of revenge were common on prairie, desert, and mountain range, the Bents and their partners kept peace with the tribes.

Most people, white, red, or black, will play fair with their fair-dealing fellow men.

20

Trade Troubles

THE END OF THE TRAIL DID NOT NECESSARILY
mean that the travelers' problems were over.
They may have thought that they had encoun-
tered all possible kinds of trouble while in the
wilds. They were wrong. The Mexicans had some
new varieties awaiting them.

At first the Mexicans were eager for the trade goods from the North. Nothing was too good for the Americano wagonmen. No price was too high to pay.

High grade cloth sold for twenty dollars a yard. Cotton goods, bought for a few cents a yard, brought as many dollars in the Mexican market place. Nails went for five cents apiece. Tobacco brought three dollars a pound. One hundred per cent profit on an investment was regarded as poor business. Sometimes it rose as high as a thousand per cent.

New Mexico elected a governor, Don Manuel Armijo. He did not like Americanos. But he was very fond of money. The Americanos had money, plenty of it. If they wanted to trade in Santa Fe, it was proper that they should pay for it. He slapped a tax of $500 per wagon on traffic from the north. It was a flat tax; a small, two-mule wagon paid as much as the largest prairie schooner.

Soon the small vehicles vanished from the trail. The large ones grew larger. Governor Armijo then levied duties on the goods, as high as one hundred per cent. Eight-cent cotton paid fifteen cents a yard.

The Armijo policy did not kill the goose that laid the golden eggs. It merely raised the price of the eggs.

"If the Mexicans can boost taxes, we can boost prices," said the traders, and they did.

The Mexican people paid the fancy prices. Governor Armijo got rich, which was the purpose of his taxes all along.

He still did not like the Americanos. An edict of 1824 forbade foreigners to hunt or trap in Mexican territory. The trappers knew the answer to that, too. Some of them applied for Mexican citizenship.

Armijo took to throwing Americans into jail and taking their merchandise. Doubtless he had some excuse. The country was filling up with hunters and trappers from the United States.

James M. Baird, who had been jailed by the Spaniards in 1812, protested these raids to the United States Government. He declared that the Americans and English were taking one hundred thousand dollars' worth of furs, mostly beaver, out of Mexican territory every year. Baird was one of those who had given up his citizenship to become a Mexican. He wanted his share of beaver skins, and he claimed that the interlopers were killing off the valuable animals. Doubtless he was right. There were few men among the pioneers who were interested in preserving wild life.

Although he acted within his legal rights, Governor Armijo was neither tactful nor honest. He arrested Ewing Young and took from him twenty thousand dollars in furs. Some of them belonged to Milton Sublette, an independent-minded member of Young's band. When the skins, now owned by the Mexican authorities, were put out to air, Sublette quietly picked up his lot, put them on his shoulders, and walked away.

The governor called out the municipal guard to arrest Sublette. The other trappers lined up with their rifles and issued an "over-our-dead-bodies" warning. There were fully a hundred armed Americans in Santa Fe, none of whom liked Armijo any better than he liked them. The chances of trouble between Mexico and the

United States were plain. Young solved the immediate difficulty by giving himself up to the authorities.

He was jailed for violating the edict of 1824. An unexpected difficulty arose. Nowhere could a copy of the edict be found. It had vanished. Ewing Young was freed, but he never got his furs back. Just to show that he had no hard feelings, he applied for Mexican citizenship the next year. More fearless, or perhaps more patriotic, Sublette hung onto both his American citizenship and his beaver skins.

A later expedition, with two thousand beaver skins taken in Mexican territory, shrewdly hid them in an abandoned mine. There the furs remained until the mountain men had made the arrangements for bribing the governor and the customs officials. That was one way to do business with Mexico. But it bred bad feeling between the two nations and undoubtedly did much to bring on the Mexican War.

Meantime, the Santa Fe Trail was becoming almost crowded. Both Santa Fe trails, indeed, for many expeditions now cut across the Cimarron

Desert where Becknell and afterward the Jedediah Smith expedition so nearly came to grief.

The Santa Fe Trail became as much of a craze as the Lost Cities of Cibola had been, and on a larger scale and with better reason. Companies were raised in the East to go after the easy money that was supposed to be there. Tenderfeet sold their farms or quit their businesses to sink their capital in the overland wagon trains. Between 1828 and 1836, one hundred seventy passports were issued to profit-dazzled adventurers. Nobody knows how many other ventures crossed the boundary without permit or passport.

The wagons grew larger and larger. The trains grew longer and longer. Oxen were introduced to the trail. They were slow, and they had tender hoofs. The drivers learned how to make buffalo-hide moccasins for them. Thus protected, the oxen plodded along at two miles per hour, pulling more weight than the stoutest mule could haul. Commercially, they did not work out as well as either horses or mules. The market price was low. An ox sold at trail's end would not fetch much more than ten dollars.

Risks of the trail persisted. The Indians did less raiding, but just as much thieving. Also they became sharper at a bargain. Disease attacked the wagon trains—smallpox and cholera.

Because wagons often arrived with goods, the Mexicans could afford to wait for a low price before buying. Thus, competition brought prices down. Many of the best beaver and otter rivers had been cleared of animals by the fur-hungry mountain men. The newcomers had to fall back on fox and muskrat, by no means so profitable. The days of one thousand per cent return in the Santa Fe market were gone forever.

The Santa Fe Trail was strewn with the bones of animals and the lost fortunes of men.

21

The Broad Way West

THE TRAIL BECOMES A ROAD. THE ROAD BECOMES
a highway. The highway opens new regions to
traffic. Traffic increases beyond the capacity of
the mules that pack it and the wagons that carry
it. Railroads are built. The original trail is abandoned, wiped out, forgotten.

So it was with the Santa Fe Trail. It more than fulfilled its purpose. For it helped this nation in its westward growth: something that would never have entered Captain William Becknell's restless mind. He wanted only to roll his wagons to Santa Fe. He did it and the boundary of his country rolled after him. His success was a major factor in the history of American expansion.

Captain Becknell died in his bed in 1832. By that time there were probably twenty-five thousand Americans in the Mexican Southwest. Many had come in by his trail. Alarmed by the invasion, the Mexican authorities closed its borders to newcomers from the United States. They suspected that the Americanos would prove to be troublemakers. They were right. In 1836 Texas raised the Lone Star flag and declared its independence.

The rambunctious Texans were not satisfied with being free from Mexico. They wanted to pass the blessings of independence on to their neighbors. They organized an invasion in 1841 and marched into New Mexico. The theory seems to have been that three hundred Texans could lick any number of Mexicans. They issued a *pronunciamento*:

"Throw off your shackles; come in with us."

The Mexicans did not accept the invitation. They captured the little force and threw them in jail, as they had every right to do. There was a great hoopla in the United States over the "wrongs" suffered by the invaders. It contributed to the bad feeling which brought on the Mexican War in 1846.

Seldom, if ever, is any nation one hundred per cent right in its dispute with another nation. Rights and wrongs are so evenly balanced in the 1846 issue that a reasonable estimate would be fifty-fifty. The important factor, which leads straight back to the Becknell wagons, is that the trade-hungry "Yanquis" wanted more trade. The Mexicans stood in the way of trade. Therefore, let's take the trade anyway, and the land with it, said the Americans.

The United States declared war. Santa Fe was captured without a fight on August 18, 1846, and the victorious General Kearny marched on to the Pacific and raised the Stars and Stripes over California.

Year after year, Becknell's wagon-tracks were broadened until they became a 250-foot wide road. Stage coach lines were established. They charged $250 per passenger from the Missouri River to Santa Fe.

Half a million dollars in cargo yearly rolled over the route. But the growing commercial importance of California tended to divert traffic from Santa Fe. The city which had once been the glowing dream of the pioneers was almost forgotten in the gold fever of 1849.

It was still a powerful name. The little railroad which in 1868 thrust westward from Topeka seventeen miles to Carbondale, took New Mexico for its goal, and called itself the Atchison, Topeka, and Santa Fe. Mile after mile the steel rails pushed westward to Santa Fe—and beyond it. Santa Fe was sidetracked. Today it is a dreamy city in a high and lovely country. But it is no longer the goal for anyone but sun-seeking winter tourists.

The Santa Fe Trail is wiped out. It is doubtful

whether a single one of the original landmarks could be found. The once deadly Jornada del Muerto is threaded by highways. The wagons are gone. The buffalo are gone. The Indians are gone, except the souvenir-selling remnants who are seen at the railroad stations and along the automobile routes. The few survivors of the beaver and otter hoards have withdrawn to remote fastnesses. Their great-great-grandfathers, whose pelts brought a few dollars, would be surprised and flattered at the present market price of their fur.

The pioneers are almost gone. Not quite. For in the back country there are still lone-hand prospectors and trappers. Their mules are equipped and packed in the same fashion as the animals of the old *atajo*. Their lives—men and mules—are not so different. There may even be left some of the old rugged, restless, pioneer spirit which pushed Captain Becknell's wagons through to Santa Fe one hundred and thirty years ago.